PUFFIN BOOKS
CRAZY TIMES WITH UNCLE KEN

Born in Kasauli, Himachal Pradesh, in 1934, Ruskin Bond grew up in
Jamnagar (Gujarat), Dehradun, New Delhi and Simla. His first novel,
The Room on the Roof, written when he was seventeen, received the John
Llewellyn Rhys Memorial Prize in 1957. Since then he has written over
three hundred short stories, essays and novellas (including *Vagrants in the
Valley* and *A Flight of Pigeons*) and more than thirty books for children. He
received the Sahitya Akademi Award for English writing in India in 1993,
and the Padma Shri in 1999.

He lives in Landour, Mussoorie, with his extended family.

Crazy Times with Uncle Ken

RUSKIN BOND

Illustrations by
Vivek Thakkar

PUFFIN BOOKS

PUFFIN BOOKS
Published by the Penguin Group
Penguin Books India Pvt. Ltd, 11 Community Centre, Panchsheel Park,
New Delhi 110 017, India
Penguin Group (USA) Inc., 375 Hudson Street, New York, New York 10014,
USA
Penguin Group (Canada), 90 Eglinton Avenue East, Suite 700, Toronto,
Ontario, M4P 2Y3, Canada (a division of Pearson Penguin Canada Inc.)
Penguin Books Ltd, 80 Strand, London WC2R 0RL, England
Penguin Ireland, 25 St. Stephen's Green, Dublin 2, Ireland (a division of
Penguin Books Ltd)
Penguin Group (Australia), 250 Camberwell Road, Camberwell, Victoria
3124, Australia (a division of Pearson Australia Group Pty Ltd)
Penguin Group (NZ), 67 Apollo Drive, Rosedale, Auckland 0632,
New Zealand (a division of Pearson New Zealand Ltd)
Penguin Group (South Africa) (Pty) Ltd, 24 Sturdee Avenue, Rosebank,
Johannesburg 2196, South Africa

Penguin Books Ltd, Registered Offices: 80 Strand, London WC2R 0RL,
England

First published in Puffin by Penguin Books India 2011

Text copyright © Ruskin Bond 2011
Illustrations copyright © Vivek Thakkar 2011

All rights reserved

10 9 8 7 6 5 4 3 2

ISBN 9780143331353

Typeset in Sabon MT by Eleven Arts, Keshav Puram, New Delhi 110035

Printed at Replika Press Pvt. Ltd, Sonepat

Contents

Introduction   vii

The Garden of Memories   1

Life with Uncle Ken   12

A Bicycle Ride with Uncle Ken   45

The Zigzag Walk   54

White Mice   58

The Ghost Who Got In   65

Monkey Trouble   81

Uncle Ken's Feathered Foes   97

A Crow for All Seasons   104

Uncle Ken Goes Birdwatching   130

Uncle Ken's Rumble in the Jungle   141

At Sea with Uncle Ken   149

Introduction

Uncle Ken would have been pleased with all the attention he's getting—a whole book to himself, chronicling his deeds and misdeeds, adventures and misadventures.

Did he really exist, I am sometimes asked.

Yes, I did have an Uncle Ken who helped to enliven my boyhood days. I'm afraid he did not set a good example for a growing boy. His jobs did not last very long, his grandiose schemes were unsuccessful, and he got both of us into trouble on more than one occasion. But he was well meaning and tried his best. We must forgive him his faults.

Also, we have to remember that he lived under the dominion of several strong-minded women—his mother (my grandmother), four sisters (my intimidating aunts and my mother), and several cousins and nieces. So he needed an ally, and sometimes he found one in me.

In his later years, when most of the family were settled abroad, Uncle Ken left for the United Kingdom, where he found a job that suited him down to the ground—a village postman.

He was given a bike (he loved bicycles), and every day he made the rounds of a pretty English village (Kintbury in Berkshire), delivering letters, parcels, bills, etc. on behalf of Her Majesty's postal service.

Uncle Ken became quite popular locally, and some evenings he would sit in the local pub and regale the other customers with hair-raising tales of his exploits in faraway India—hunting man-eating tigers or crocodiles, climbing mountain peaks in the Himalayas, rescuing princesses from bands of dacoits, or playing cricket with the great Ranji (forgetting that Ranji played most of his cricket in England and for England!). His listeners did not always believe him, but they enjoyed listening to his tall tales and were happy to pay for his drinks.

Tall tales he might have told, but the tales in *this* book are true. (Or almost true.) If the stories in this collection are described by the publishers as 'fiction', it is because they know that if they were called 'non-fiction', no one would believe them. 'Stranger than fiction' is probably best.

But Uncle Ken was real, and you will find his name embedded in the rolls of at least two old public schools in India. He was expelled from both of them. In one instance, he put on a wig and impersonated a lady teacher—so successfully that he was able to gain admittance to the girls' dormitory before being discovered. In the other instance—in his next school—he celebrated Diwali by setting off firecrackers in the chemistry lab and causing an explosion that shattered several windows and gave the science master a nervous breakdown.

After that no school would have him. So Uncle Ken proceeded to educate himself, learning a few things from Grandfather (his Dad), including the art of survival.

Surviving . . . he was good at that.

So perhaps we can learn something from him, after all. In a world that has no time for losers, to be a survivor is something of an achievement.

The Garden of Memories

Sitting in the sun on a winter's afternoon, feeling my age just a little (I'm over seventy), I began reminiscing about my boyhood in the Dehra of long ago, and found myself missing the old times—friends of my youth, my grandmother, our neighbours, interesting characters in our small town, and, of course, my eccentric relative—the dashing young Uncle Ken!

Yes, Dehra was a small town then—uncluttered, uncrowded, with quiet lanes and pretty gardens and shady orchards.

The only time in my life that I was fortunate enough to live in a house with a real garden—as opposed to a backyard or balcony or windswept veranda—was during those three years when I spent my winter holidays (December to March) in Granny's bungalow on the Old Survey Road.

The best months were February and March, when the garden was heavy with the scent of sweet peas, the flower beds a many-coloured quilt of phlox, antirrhinum, larkspur, petunia and Californian poppy. I loved the bright yellows of the Californian poppies, the soft pinks of our own Indian poppies, the subtle perfume of petunias and snapdragons and, above all, the delicious, overpowering scent of the massed sweet peas which grew taller than me.

Flowers made a sensualist of me. They taught me the delight of smell, colour and touch—yes, touch too, for to press a rose to one's lips is very like a gentle, hesitant, exploratory kiss . . .

Granny decided on what flowers should be sown, and where. Dhuki, the gardener, did the digging and weeding, sowing and transplanting. He was a skinny, taciturn old man, who had begun to resemble the weeds he flung away. He did not mind answering my questions, but never did he allow our brief conversations to interfere with his work. Most of the time he was to be found on his haunches, hoeing and weeding with a little spade called a *khurpi*. He would throw out the smaller marigolds because he said Granny did not care for them. I felt sorry for these colourful little discards, collected them and transplanted them to a little garden patch of my own at the back of the house, near the garden wall.

Another so-called weed that I liked was a little purple flower that grew in clusters all over Dehra, on any bit of wasteland, in ditches, on canal banks. It flowered from late winter into early summer, and it will be growing in the valley and beyond long after gardens have become obsolete, as indeed they must, considering the rapid spread of urban clutter. It brightens up fields and roads where you least expect a little colour. I have since learnt that it is called *Ageratum*, and that it is actually prized as a garden flower in Europe, where it is described as 'Blue Mink' in the seed catalogues. Here it isn't blue but purple, and it grows all the way from Rajpur (just above Dehra) to the outskirts of Meerut; then it disappears.

Other garden outcasts include the lantana bush, an attractive wayside shrub; the thorn apple, various thistles, daisies and dandelions. But both Granny and Dhuki had declared a war on weeds, and many of these commoners had to exist outside the confines of the garden. Like slum children, they survived rather well in ditches and on the roadside, while their more pampered fellow citizens were prone to leaf diseases and parasitic infections of various kinds.

The veranda was a place where Granny herself could potter about, attending to various ferns, potted palms and colourful geraniums. She averred that geraniums kept snakes away, although she never said why. As far as I know, snakes don't have a great sense of smell.

One day I saw a snake curled up at the bottom of the veranda steps. When it saw me, or became aware of my footsteps, it uncoiled itself and slithered away. I told Granny about it, and observed that it did not seem to be bothered by the geraniums.

'Ah,' said Granny. 'But for those geraniums, the snake would have entered the house!' There was no arguing with Granny. Or with Uncle Ken, when he was at his most pontifical.

One day, while walking near the canal bank, we came upon a green grass snake holding a frog in its mouth. The frog was half in, half out, and with the help of my hockey stick, I made the snake disgorge the unfortunate creature. It hopped away, none the worse for its adventure.

I felt quite pleased with myself. 'Is this what it feels like to be god?' I mused aloud.

'No,' said Uncle Ken. 'God would have let the snake finish its lunch.'

Uncle Ken was one of those people who went through life without having to do much, although a great deal seemed to happen around him. He acted as a sort of catalyst for events that involved the family, friends, neighbours, the town itself. He believed in the fruits of hard work: other people's hard work.

Ken was good looking as a boy, and his sisters (including my mother, the youngest) doted on him. He took full advantage of their devotion, and, as the girls grew up and married, Ken took it for granted that they and their husbands would continue to look after his welfare. You could say he was the originator of the welfare state: his own.

I'll say this for Uncle Ken, he had a large fund of curiosity in his nature, and he loved to explore the town we lived in, and any other town or city where he might happen to find himself. With one sister settled in Lucknow, another in Ranchi, a third in Bhopal and a fourth in Simla, Uncle Ken managed to see a cross section of India by dividing his time between all his sisters and their long-suffering husbands.

Uncle Ken liked to walk. Occasionally he borrowed my bicycle, but he had a tendency to veer off the main road and into ditches and other obstacles after a collision with a bullock cart, in which he tore his trousers and damaged the handlebar of my bicycle. He concluded that walking was the best way of getting around Dehra.

Uncle Ken dressed quite smartly for a man of no particular occupation. He had a blue-striped blazer and a red-striped blazer; he usually wore white or off-white trousers, immaculately pressed (by Granny). He was the delight of shoeshine boys, for he would always have his shoes polished. Summers he wore a straw hat, telling everyone he had worn it for the Varsity Boat Race while rowing for Oxford (he hadn't been to England, let alone Oxford); winters he wore one of Grandfather's old felt hats. He seldom went bareheaded. At thirty he was almost completely bald, prompting Aunt Mabel to remark: 'Well, Ken, you must be grateful for small mercies. At least you'll never have bats getting entangled in your hair.'

Thanks to all his walking Uncle Ken had a good digestion, which kept pace with a hearty appetite. Our walks would be punctuated by short stops at chaat shops, sweet shops, fruit stalls, confectioners, small bakeries and other eateries.

'Have you brought any pocket money along?' he would ask, for he was usually broke.

'Granny gave me five rupees.'

'We'll try some rasgullas, then.'

And the rasgullas would be followed by gulab jamuns until my five rupees was finished. Uncle Ken received a small allowance from Granny, but he ferreted it away to spend on clothes, preferring to spend my pocket money on perishables such as ice creams, kulfis and Indian sweets.

On one occasion, when neither of us had any money, Uncle Ken decided to venture into a sugar cane field on the outskirts of the town. He had broken off a stick of cane, and was busy chewing on it, when the owner of the field spotted us and let out a volley of imprecations. We fled from the field with the irate farmer giving chase. I could run faster than Uncle Ken, and did so. The farmer would have caught up with Uncle Ken if the latter's hat hadn't blown off, causing a diversion. The farmer picked up the hat, examined it, seemed to fancy it, and put it on. Several small boys clapped and cheered. The farmer marched off, wearing the hat, and Uncle Ken wisely decided against making any attempt to retrieve it.

'I'll get another one,' he said philosophically.

He wore a pith helmet, or sola-topee, for the next few days, as he thought it would protect him from sticks and stones. For a while he harboured a paranoia that all the sugar cane farmers in the valley were looking for him, to avenge his foray into their fields. But after some time he discarded the topee because, according to him, it interfered with his good looks.

*

Granny grew the best sweet peas in Dehra. But she never entered them at the Annual Flower Show held every year in the second week of March. She did not grow flowers to win prizes, she said; she grew them to please the spirit of Grandfather, who still hovered about the house and grounds he'd built thirty years earlier.

Miss Kellner, Granny's crippled but valued tenant, said the flowers were grown to attract beautiful butterflies, and she was right. In early summer, swarms of butterflies flitted about the garden.

Uncle Ken had no compunction about winning prizes, even though he did nothing to deserve them. Without telling anyone, he submitted a large display of Granny's sweet peas for the flower show, and when the prizes were announced, lo and behold! Kenneth Clerke had been awarded first prize for his magnificent display of sweet peas.

Granny refused to speak to him for several days.

Uncle Ken had been hoping for a cash prize, but they gave him a flower vase. He told me it was a Ming vase. But it looked more like Meerut to me. He offered it to Granny, hoping to propitiate her; but, still displeased with him, she gave it to Mr Khastgir, the artist next door, who kept his paintbrushes in it.

Although I was sometimes a stubborn and unruly boy (my hero was Richmal Crompton's 'William'), I got on well with old ladies, especially those who, like Miss Kellner, were fond of offering me chocolates, marzipans, soft nankhatai biscuits (made at Yusuf's bakery in the Dilaram Bazaar), and pieces of crystallized ginger. Miss Kellner couldn't walk—had never walked—and so she could only admire the garden from a distance, but it was from her that I learnt the names of many flowers, trees, birds and even butterflies.

Uncle Ken wasn't any good at names, but he wanted to catch a rare butterfly. He said he could make a fortune if he caught a leaf butterfly called the Purple Emperor. He equipped himself with a butterfly net, a bottle of ether, and a cabinet for mounting his trophies; he then prowled all over the grounds, making frequent forays at anything that flew.

He caught several common species—Red Admirals, a Tortoiseshell, a Painted Lady, even the occasional dragonfly—but the high-flying Purple Emperor and other exotics eluded him, as did the fortune he was always aspiring to make.

Eventually he caught an angry wasp, which stung him through the netting. Chased by its fellow wasps, he took refuge in the lily pond and emerged sometime later draped in lilies and water weeds.

After this, Uncle Ken retired from the butterfly business, insisting that tiger-hunting was safer.

Life with Uncle Ken

Granny's fabulous kitchen

As kitchens went, it wasn't all that big. It wasn't as big as the bedroom or the living room, but it was big enough, and there was a pantry next to it. What made it fabulous was all that came out of it: good things to eat like cakes and curries, chocolate fudge and peanut toffee, jellies and jam tarts, meat pies, stuffed turkeys, stuffed chickens, stuffed eggplants, and hams stuffed with stuffed chickens.

As far as I was concerned, Granny was the best cook in the whole wide world.

Two generations of Clerkes had lived in India and my maternal grandmother had settled in a small town in the foothills, just where the great plain ended and the Himalayas began. The town was called Dehradun. It's still there, though much bigger and busier now. Granny had a house—a large rambling bungalow—on the

outskirts of the town, on Old Survey Road. In
the grounds were many trees, most of them fruit
trees. Mangoes, litchis, guavas, bananas, papaya,
lemons—there was room for all of them, including
a giant jackfruit tree casting its shadow on the walls
of the house.

> Blessed is the house upon whose walls
> The shade of an old tree softly falls.

I remember those lines of Granny's. They were
true words, because it was a good house to live in,
especially for a nine year old with a tremendous
appetite. If Granny was the best cook in the world,
I must have been the boy with the best appetite.

Every winter, when I came home from boarding
school, I would spend about a month with Granny
before going on to spend the rest of the holidays
with my mother and stepfather. My parents couldn't
cook. They employed a khansama—a professional
cook—who made a good mutton curry but little else.
Mutton curry for lunch and mutton curry for dinner
can be a bit tiring, especially for a boy who liked to
eat almost everything.

Granny was glad to have me because she lived

alone most of the time. Not entirely alone, though . . . There was a gardener, Dhuki, who lived in an outhouse. And he had a son called Mohan, who was about my age. And there was Ayah, an elderly maidservant, who helped with the household work. And there was a Siamese cat with bright blue eyes, and a mongrel dog called Crazy because he ran circles round the house.

And, of course, there was Uncle Ken, Granny's only son, who came to stay whenever he was out of a job (which was quite often) or when he felt like enjoying some of Granny's cooking.

So Granny wasn't really alone. All the same, she was glad to have me. She didn't enjoy cooking for herself, she said; she had to cook for *someone*. And although the cat and the dog and sometimes Uncle Ken appreciated her efforts, a good cook likes to have a boy to feed, because boys are adventurous and ready to try the most unusual dishes.

Whenever Granny tried out a new recipe on me, she would wait for my comments and reactions, and then make a note in one of her exercise books. These notes were useful when she made the dish again, or when she tried it out on others.

'Do you like it?' she'd ask, after I'd taken a few mouthfuls.

'Yes, Gran.'

'Sweet enough.'

'Yes, Gran.'

'Not *too* sweet.'

'No, Gran.'

'Would you like some more?'

'Yes, please, Gran.'

'Well, finish it off.'

'If you say so, Gran.'

Roast duck. This was one of Granny's specials. The first time I had roast duck at Granny's place, Uncle Ken was there too.

He'd just lost a job as a railway guard, and had come to stay with Granny until he could find another job. He always stayed as long as he could, only moving on when Granny offered to get him a job as an assistant master in Padre Lal's Academy for Small Boys. Uncle Ken couldn't stand small boys. They made him nervous, he said. I made him nervous too, but there was only one of me, and there was always Granny to protect him. At Padre Lal's, there were over a hundred small boys.

Although Uncle Ken had a tremendous appetite, and ate just as much as I did, he never praised Granny's dishes. I think this is why I was annoyed with him at times, and why sometimes I enjoyed making him feel nervous.

Uncle Ken looked down at the roast duck, his glasses slipping down to the edge of his nose.

'Hm . . . Duck again?'

'What do you mean, duck again? You haven't had duck since you were here last month,' retorted Granny.

'That's what I mean,' said Uncle Ken. 'Somehow, one expects more variety from you.'

All the same, he took two large helpings and ate most of the stuffing before I could get at it. I took my revenge by emptying all the apple sauce on to my plate. Uncle Ken knew I loved the stuffing; and I knew he was crazy about Granny's apple sauce. So we were even.

'When are you joining your parents?' he asked hopefully, over the jam tart.

'I may not go to them this year,' I said. 'When are you getting another job, Uncle?'

'Oh, I'm thinking of taking rest for a couple of months.'

I enjoyed helping Granny and Ayah with the washing up. While we were at work, Uncle Ken would take a siesta on the veranda or switch on the radio to listen to dance music. Glenn Miller and his swing band was all the rage then.

'And how do you like your Uncle Ken?' asked Granny one day, as she emptied the bones from his plate into the dog's bowl.

'I wish he was someone else's uncle,' I said.

'He's not so bad, really. Just eccentric.'

'What's eccentric?'

'Oh, just a little crazy.'

'At least Crazy runs round the house,' I said. 'I've never seen Uncle Ken running.'

But I did one day.

Mohan and I were playing marbles in the shade of the mango grove when we were taken aback by the sight of Uncle Ken charging across the compound, pursued by a swarm of bees. He'd been smoking a cigar under a silk-cotton tree, and the fumes had disturbed the wild bees in their hive, directly above him. Uncle Ken fled indoors and leapt into a tub of cold water. He had received a few stings and decided to remain in bed for three days. Ayah took his meals to him on a tray.

'I didn't know Uncle Ken could run so fast,' I said later that day.

'It's nature's way of compensating,' said Granny.

'What's compensating?'

'Making up for things . . . Now at least Uncle Ken knows that he can run. Isn't that wonderful?'

*

Whenever Granny made vanilla or chocolate fudge, she gave me some to take to Mohan, the gardener's son. It was no use taking him roast duck or curried chicken because in his house no one ate meat. But Mohan liked sweets—Indian sweets, which were made with lots of milk and lots of sugar, as well as Granny's home-made English sweets.

We would climb into the branches of the jackfruit tree and eat fudge or peppermints or sticky toffee. We couldn't eat the jackfruit, except when it was cooked as a vegetable or made into a pickle. But the tree itself was wonderful for climbing. And some wonderful creatures lived in it—squirrels and fruit bats and a pair of green parrots. The squirrels were friendly and soon got into the habit of eating from our hands. They, too, were fond of chocolate fudge.

One young squirrel would even explore my pockets to see if I was keeping anything from him.

Mohan and I could climb almost any tree in the garden, and if Granny was looking for us, she'd call from the front veranda and then from the back veranda and then from the pantry at the side of the house and, finally, from the bathroom window on the other side of the house. There were trees on all sides and it was impossible to tell which one we were in, until we answered her call. Sometimes Crazy would give us away by barking beneath our tree.

When there was fruit to be picked, Mohan did the picking. The mangoes and litchis came into season during the summer, when I was away at boarding school, so I couldn't help with the fruit gathering. The papayas were in season during the winter, but you don't climb papaya trees; they are too slender and wobbly. You knock the papayas down with a long pole.

Mohan also helped Granny with the pickling. She was justly famous for her pickles. Green mangoes, pickled in oil, were always popular. So was her hot lime pickle. And she was equally good at pickling turnips, carrots, cauliflowers, chillies and other fruits and vegetables. She could pickle almost anything, from a nasturtium seed to a jackfruit. Uncle Ken didn't care for pickles, so I was always urging Granny to make more of them.

My own preference was for sweet chutneys and sauces, but I ate pickles too, even the very hot ones.

One winter, when Granny's funds were low, Mohan and I went from house to house, selling pickles for her.

In spite of all the people and pets she fed, Granny wasn't rich. The house had come to her from Grandfather, but there wasn't much money in the bank. The mango crop brought in a fair amount every year, and there was a small pension from the Railways (Grandfather had been one of the pioneers who'd helped bring the railway line to Dehra at the turn of the century), but there was no other income. And now that I come to think of it, all those wonderful meals consisted only of the one course, followed by a sweet dish. It was Granny's cooking that turned a modest meal into a feast.

I wasn't ashamed to sell pickles for Granny. It was great fun. Mohan and I armed ourselves with baskets filled with pickle bottles, then set off to cover all the houses in our area.

Major Wilkie, across the road, was our first customer. He had a red beard and bright blue eyes and was almost always good-humoured.

'And what have you got there, young Bond?' he asked.

'Pickle, sir.'

'Pickles! Have you been making them?'

'No, sir, they're my grandmother's. We're selling them, so we can buy a turkey for Christmas.'

'Mrs Clerke's pickles, eh? Well, I'm glad mine is the first house on your way, because I'm sure that basket will soon be empty. There is no one who can make a pickle like your grandmother, son. I've said it before and I'll say it again, she's god's gift to a world that's terribly short of good cooks. My wife's gone shopping, so I can talk quite freely, you see . . . What have you got this time? Stuffed chillies, I trust. She knows they're my favourite. I shall be deeply wounded if there are not stuffed chillies in the basket.'

There were, in fact, three bottles of stuffed red chillies in the basket, and Major Wilkie took all of them.

Our next call was at Miss Kellner's house. Miss Kellner couldn't eat hot food, so it was no use offering her pickles. But she bought a bottle of preserved ginger. And she gave me a little prayer book. Whenever I went to see her, she gave me a new prayer book. Soon I had quite a collection of prayer books. What was I to do with them? Finally, Uncle Ken took them off me, and sold them back to Miss Kellner.

Further down the road, Dr Dutt, who was in charge of the hospital, bought several bottles of lime pickles, saying it was good for his liver. And Mr Hari, who owned a garage at the end of the road and sold all the latest cars, bought two bottles of pickled onions and begged us to bring him another two the following month.

By the time we got home, the basket would usually be empty and Granny richer by twenty or thirty rupees—enough, in those days, for a turkey.

'It's high time you found a job,' said Granny to Uncle Ken one day.

'There are no jobs in Dehra,' complained Uncle Ken.

'How can you tell? You've never looked for one. And anyway, you don't have to stay here forever. Your sister Emily is headmistress of a school in Lucknow. You could go to her. She said before that she was ready to put you in charge of a dormitory.'

'Bah!' said Uncle Ken. 'Honestly, you don't expect me to look after a dormitory seething with forty or fifty demented small boys?'

'What's demented?' I asked.

'Shut up,' said Uncle Ken.

'It means crazy,' said Granny.

'So many words mean crazy,' I complained. 'Why don't we just say crazy. We have a crazy dog, and now Uncle Ken is crazy too.'

Uncle Ken clipped me over my ear, and Granny said, 'Your uncle isn't crazy, so don't be disrespectful. He's just lazy.'

'And eccentric,' I said. 'I heard he was eccentric.'

'Who said I was eccentric?' demanded Uncle Ken.

'Miss Leslie,' I lied. I knew Uncle Ken was fond of Miss Leslie, who ran a beauty parlour in Dehra's smart shopping centre, Astley Hall.

'I don't believe you,' said Uncle Ken. 'Anyway, when did you see Miss Leslie?'

'We sold her a bottle of mint chutney last week. I told her you liked mint chutney. But she said she'd bought it for Mr Brown who's taking her to the pictures tomorrow.'

*

'Eat well, but don't overeat,' Granny used to tell me. 'Good food is a gift from god, and like any other gift, it can be misused.'

She'd made a list of kitchen proverbs and pinned it to the pantry door—not so high that I couldn't read it, either.

These were some of the proverbs:

Light suppers make long lives.
Better a small fish than an empty dish.
There is skill in all things, even in making
   porridge.
Eating and drinking should not keep men from
   thinking.
Dry bread at home is better than roast meat
   abroad.
A good dinner sharpens the wit and softens
   the heart.
Let not your tongue cut your throat.

Uncle Ken does nothing

To our surprise, Uncle Ken got a part-time job as a guide, showing tourist the 'sights' around Dehra.

There was an old fort near the river bed; and a seventeenth-century temple; and a jail where Pandit

Nehru had spent some time as a political prisoner; and, about ten miles into the foothills, the hot sulphur springs.

Uncle Ken told us he was taking a party of six American tourists, husbands and wives, to the sulphur springs. Granny was pleased. Uncle Ken was busy at last! She gave him a hamper filled with ham sandwiches, home-made biscuits and a dozen oranges—ample provision for a day's outing.

The sulphur springs were only ten miles from Dehra, but we didn't see Uncle Ken for three days.

He was a sight when he got back. His clothes were dusty and torn; his cheeks were sunken; and the little bald patch on top of his head had been burnt a bright red.

'What have you been doing to yourself?' asked Granny.

Uncle Ken sank into the armchair on the veranda. 'I'm starving, Mother. Give me something to eat.'

'What happened to the food you took with you?'

'There were seven of us, and it was all finished on the first day.'

'Well, it was only supposed to last a day. You said you were going to the sulphur springs.'

'Yes, that's where we were going,' said Uncle Ken. 'But we never reached them. We got lost in the hills.'

'How could you possibly have got lost in the hills? You had only to walk straight along the river bed and up the valley . . . You ought to know, you were the guide and you'd been there before, when your father was alive.'

'Yes, I know,' said Uncle Ken, looking crestfallen. 'But I forgot the way. That is, I forgot the valley. I mean, I took them up the wrong valley. And I kept thinking the springs would be at the same river, but it wasn't the same river . . . So we kept walking, until we were in the hills, and then I looked down and saw we'd come up the wrong valley. We had to spend the night under the stars. It was very, very cold. And next day I thought we'd come back a quicker way, through Mussoorie, but we took the wrong path and reached Kempti instead . . . And then we walked down to the motor road and caught a bus.'

I helped Granny put Uncle Ken to bed, and then helped her make him a strengthening onion soup. I took him the soup on a tray, and he made a face while drinking it and then asked for more. He was in bed for two days, while Ayah and I took turns taking him his meals. He wasn't a bit grateful.

*

When Uncle Ken complained he was losing his hair and that his bald patch was increasing in size, Granny looked up her book of old recipes and said there was one for baldness which Grandfather had used with great success. It consisted of a lotion made with gherkins soaked in brandy. Uncle Ken said he'd try it.

Granny soaked some gherkins in brandy for a week, then gave the bottle to Uncle Ken with instructions to rub a little into his scalp mornings and evenings.

Next day, when she looked into his room, she found only gherkins in the bottle. Uncle Ken had drunk all the brandy.

*

Uncle Ken liked to whistle.

Hands in his pockets, nothing to do, he would stroll about the house, around the garden, up and down the road, whistling feebly to himself.

It was always the same whistle, tuneless to everyone except my uncle.

'What are you whistling today, Uncle Ken?' I'd ask.

'"Ol' Man River". Don't you recognize it?'

And the next time around he'd be whistling the same notes, and I'd say, 'Still whistling "Ol' Man River", Uncle?'

'No, I'm not. This is "Danny Boy". Can't you tell the difference?'

And he'd slouch off, whistling tunelessly.

Sometimes it irritated Granny.

'Can't you stop whistling, Ken? It gets on my nerves. Why don't you try singing for a change?'

'I can't. It's "The Blue Danube"; there aren't any words,' and he'd waltz around the kitchen, whistling.

'Well, you can do your whistling and waltzing on the veranda,' Granny would say. 'I won't have it in the kitchen. It spoils the food.'

When Uncle Ken had a bad tooth removed by our dentist, Dr Kapadia, we thought his whistling would stop. But it only became louder and shriller.

One day, while he was strolling along the road, hands in his pockets, doing nothing, whistling very loudly, a girl on a bicycle passed him. She stopped suddenly, got off the bicycle, and blocked his way.

'If you whistle at me every time I pass, Kenneth Clerke,' she said, 'I'll wallop you!'

Uncle Ken went red in the face. 'I wasn't whistling at you,' he said.

'Well, I don't see anyone else on the road.'

'I was whistling "God Save the King". Don't you recognize it?'

Uncle Ken on the job

'We'll have to do something about Uncle Ken,' said Granny to the world at large.

I was in the kitchen with her, shelling peas and popping a few into my mouth now and then. Suzie, the Siamese cat, sat on the sideboard, patiently watching Granny prepare an Irish stew. Suzie liked Irish stew.

'It's not that I mind him staying,' said Granny, 'and I don't want any money from him, either. But it isn't healthy for a young man to remain idle for so long.'

'Is Uncle Ken a young man, Gran?'

'He's thirty. Everyone says he'll improve as he grows up.'

'He could go and live with Aunt Mabel.'

'He *does* go and live with Aunt Mabel. He also lives with Aunt Emily and Aunt Beryl. That's his trouble—he has too many doting sisters ready to put him up and put up with him . . . Their husbands are all quite well off and can afford to have him now and then. So our Ken spends three months with Mabel, three months with Beryl, three months with me. That way he gets through the year as everyone's guest and doesn't have to worry about making a living.'

'He's lucky in a way,' I said.

'His luck won't last forever. Already Mabel is talking of going to New Zealand. And once India is free—in just a year or two from now—Emily and Beryl will probably go off to England, because their husbands are in the army and all the British officers will be leaving.'

'Can't Uncle Ken follow them to England?'

'He knows he'll have to start working if he goes there. When your aunts find they have to manage without servants, they won't be ready to keep Ken for long periods. In any case, who's going to pay his fare to England or New Zealand?'

'If he can't go, he'll stay here with you, Granny. You'll be here, won't you?'

'Not forever. Only while I live.'

'You won't go to England?'

'No, I've grown up here. I'm like the trees. I've taken root, I won't be going away—not until, like an old tree, I'm without any more leaves . . . You'll go, though, when you are bigger. You'll probably finish your schooling abroad.'

'I'd rather finish it here. I want to spend all my holidays with you. If I go away, who'll look after you when you grow old?'

'I'm old already. Over sixty.'

'Is that very old? It's only a little older than Uncle Ken. And how will you look after him when you're *really* old?'

'He can look after himself if he tries. And it's time he started. It's time he took a job.'

I pondered over the problem. I could think of nothing that would suit Uncle Ken—or rather, I could think of no one who would find him suitable. It was Ayah who made a suggestion.

'The Maharani of Jetpur needs a tutor for her children,' she said. 'Just a boy and a girl.'

'How do you know?' asked Granny.

'I heard it from their ayah. The pay is two hundred rupees a month, and there is not much work—only two hours every morning.'

'That should suit Uncle Ken,' I said.

'Yes, it's a good idea,' said Granny. 'We'll have to talk him into applying. He ought to go over and see them. The Maharani is a good person to work for.'

Uncle Ken agreed to go over and enquire about the job. The Maharani was out when he called, but he was interviewed by the Maharaja.

'Do you play tennis?' asked the Maharaja.

'Yes,' said Uncle Ken, who remembered having played a bit of tennis when he was a schoolboy.

'In that case, the job's yours. I've been looking for a fourth player for a doubles match . . . By the way, were you at Cambridge?'

'No, I was at Oxford,' said Uncle Ken.

The Maharaja was impressed. An Oxford man who could play tennis was just the sort of tutor he wanted for his children.

When Uncle Ken told Granny about the interview, she said, 'But you haven't been to Oxford, Ken. How could you say that!'

'Of course I have been to Oxford. Don't you remember? I spent two years there with your brother Jim!'

'Yes, but you were helping him in his pub in the town. You weren't at the University.'

'Well, the Maharaja never asked me if I had been

to the University. He asked me if I was at Cambridge, and I said no, I was at Oxford, which was perfectly true. He didn't ask me what I was doing at Oxford. What difference does it make?'

And he strolled off, whistling.

*

To our surprise, Uncle Ken was a great success in his job. In the beginning, anyway.

The Maharaja was such a poor tennis player that he was delighted to discover that there was someone who was even worse. So, instead of becoming a doubles partner for the Maharaja, Uncle Ken became his favourite singles opponent. As long as he could keep losing to His Highness, Uncle Ken's job was safe.

In between tennis matches and accompanying his employer on duck shoots, Uncle Ken squeezed in a few lessons for the children, teaching them reading, writing and arithmetic. Sometimes he took me along, so that I could tell him when he got his sums wrong. Uncle Ken wasn't very good at subtraction, although he could add fairly well.

The Maharaja's children were smaller than me. Uncle Ken would leave me with them, saying, 'Just see that they do their sums properly, Ruskin,' and he would stroll off to the tennis courts, hands in his pockets, whistling tunelessly.

Even if his pupils had different answers to the same sum, he would give both of them an encouraging pat, saying, 'Excellent, excellent. I'm glad to see both of you trying so hard. One of you is right and one of you is wrong, but as I don't want to discourage either of you, I won't say who's right and who's wrong!'

But afterwards, on the way home, he'd ask me, 'Which was the right answer, Ruskin?'

Uncle Ken always maintained that he would never have lost his job if he hadn't beaten the Maharaja at tennis.

Not that Uncle Ken had any intention of winning. But by playing occasional games with the Maharaja's secretaries and guests, his tennis had improved and so, try as hard as he might to lose, he couldn't help winning a match against his employer.

The Maharaja was furious.

'Mr Clerke,' he said sternly, 'I don't think you realize the importance of losing. We can't all win, you know. Where would the world be without losers?'

'I'm terribly sorry,' said Uncle Ken. 'It was just a fluke, Your Highness.'

The Maharaja accepted Uncle Ken's apologies;

but a week later it happened again. Kenneth Clerke won and the Maharaja stormed off the court without saying a word. The following day he turned up at lesson time. As usual Uncle Ken and the children were engaged in a game of noughts and crosses.

'We won't be requiring your services from tomorrow, Mr Clerke. I've asked my secretary to give you a month's salary in lieu of notice.'

Uncle Ken came home with his hands in his pockets, whistling cheerfully.

'You're early,' said Granny.

'They don't need me any more,' said Uncle Ken.

'Oh well, never mind. Come in and have your tea.'

Granny must have known the job wouldn't last very long. And she wasn't one to nag. As she said later, 'At least he tried. And it lasted longer than most of his jobs—two months.'

Uncle Ken at the wheel

On my next visit to Dehra, Mohan met me at the station. We got into a tonga with my luggage and we went rattling and jingling along Dehra's quiet roads to Granny's house.

'Tell me all the news, Mohan.'

'Not much to tell. Some of the sahibs are selling their houses and going away. Suzie has had kittens.'

Granny knew I'd been in the train for two nights, and she had a huge breakfast ready for me. Porridge, scrambled eggs on toast. Bacon with fried tomatoes. Toast and marmalade. Sweet milky tea.

She told me there'd been a letter from Uncle Ken.

'He says he's the assistant manager at Firpo's hotel in Simla,' she said. 'The salary is very good, and he gets free board and lodging. It's a steady job and I hope he keeps it.'

Three days later Uncle Ken was on the veranda steps with his bedding roll and battered suitcase.

'Have you given up the hotel job?' asked Granny.

'No,' said Uncle Ken. 'They have closed down.'

'I hope it wasn't because of you.'

'No, Mother. The bigger hotels in the hill stations are all closing down.'

'Well, never mind. Come along and have your tiffin. There is a kofta curry today. It's Ruskin's favourite.'

'Oh, is he here too? I have far too many nephews and nieces. Still, he's preferable to those two girls of Mabel's. They made life miserable for me all the time I was with them in Simla.'

Over tiffin (as lunch was called in those days),

Uncle Ken talked very seriously about ways and means of earning a living.

'There is only one taxi in the whole of Dehra,' he mused. 'Surely there is business for another?'*

'I'm sure there is,' said Granny. 'But where does it get you? In the first place, you don't have a taxi. And in the second place, you can't drive.'

'I can soon learn. There's a driving school in town. And I can use Dad's old car. It's been gathering dust in the garage for years.' (He was referring to Grandfather's vintage Hillman Roadster. It was a 1926 model: about twenty years old.)

'I don't think it will run now,' said Granny.

'Of course it will. It just needs some oiling and greasing and a spot of paint.'

'All right, learn to drive. Then we will see about the Roadster.'

So Uncle Ken joined the driving school.

He was very regular, going for his lessons for an hour in the evening. Granny paid the fee.

After a month, Uncle Ken announced that he could drive and that he was taking the Roadster out for a trial run.

*In the early 1940s, Dehra had only one or two taxis. Today, there are over 500 plying in the town.

'You haven't got your licence yet,' said Granny.

'Oh, I won't take her far,' said Uncle Ken. 'Just down the road and back again.'

He spent all morning cleaning up the car. Granny gave him money for a can of petrol.

After tea, Uncle Ken said, 'Come along, Ruskin, hop in and I will give you a ride. Bring Mohan along too.'

Mohan and I needed no urging. We got into the car beside Uncle Ken.

'Now don't go too fast, Ken,' said Granny anxiously. 'You are not used to the car as yet.'

Uncle Ken nodded and smiled and gave two sharp toots on the horn. He was feeling pleased with himself.

Driving through the gate, he nearly ran over Crazy.

Miss Kellner, who was carried out to the rickshaw for her evening ride, saw Uncle Ken at the wheel of the Roadster and begged to be taken indoors.

Uncle Ken drove straight and fast, tootling the horn without a break.

At the end of the road there was a roundabout.

'We'll turn here,' said Uncle Ken, 'and then drive back again.'

He turned the steering wheel; we began going round the roundabout; but the steering wheel wouldn't turn all the way, not as much as Uncle Ken would have liked it to . . . So, instead of going round, we took a right turn and kept going, straight on—and straight through the Maharaja of Jetpur's garden wall!

It was a single-brick wall, and the Roadster knocked it down and emerged on the other side without any damage to the car or any of its occupants. Uncle Ken brought it to a halt in the middle of the Maharaja's lawn.

Running across the grass came the Maharaja himself, flanked by his secretaries and their assistants.

When he saw that it was Uncle Ken at the wheel, the Maharaja beamed with pleasure.

'Delighted to see you, old chap!' he exclaimed. 'Jolly decent of you to drop in again. How about a game of tennis?'

Uncle Ken at the wicket

Although restored to the Maharaja's favour, Uncle Ken was still without a job.

Granny refused to let him take the Hillman out again and so he decided to sulk. He said it was all

Grandfather's fault for not seeing to the steering wheel ten years ago, while he was still alive. Uncle Ken went on a hunger strike for two hours (between tiffin and tea), and we did not hear him whistle for several days.

'The blessedness of silence,' said Granny.

And then he announced that he was going to Lucknow to stay with Aunt Emily.

'She has three children and a school to look after,' said Granny. 'Don't stay too long.'

'She doesn't mind how long I stay,' said Uncle Ken and off he went.

His visit to Lucknow was a memorable one, and we only heard about it much later.

When Uncle Ken got down at Lucknow station, he found himself surrounded by a large crowd, everyone waving to him and shouting words of welcome in Hindi, Urdu and English. Before he could make out what it was all about, he was smothered by garlands of marigolds. A young man came forward and announced, 'The Gomti Cricketing Association welcomes you to the historical city of Lucknow,' and promptly led Uncle Ken out of the station to a waiting car.

It was only when the car drove into the sports'

stadium that Uncle Ken realized that he was expected to play in a cricket match.

This is what had happened.

Bruce Hallam, the famous English cricketer, was touring India and had agreed to play in a charity match at Lucknow. But the previous evening, in Delhi, Bruce had gone to bed with an upset stomach and hadn't been able to get up in time to catch the train. A telegram was sent to the organizers of the match in Lucknow; but, like many a telegram, it did not reach its destination. The cricket fans of Lucknow had arrived at the station in droves to welcome the great cricketer. And by a strange coincidence, Uncle Ken bore a startling resemblance to Bruce Hallam; even the bald patch on the crown of his head was exactly like Hallam's. Hence the muddle. And, of course, Uncle Ken was always happy to enter into the spirit of a muddle.

Having received from the Gomti Cricketing Association a rousing reception and a magnificent breakfast at the stadium, he felt that it would be very unsporting on his part if he refused to play cricket for them. 'If I can hit a tennis ball,' he mused, 'I ought to be able to hit a cricket ball.' And luckily there was a blazer and a pair of white flannels in his suitcase.

The Gomti team won the toss and decided to bat. Uncle Ken was expected to go in at number three, Bruce Hallam's normal position. And he soon found himself walking to the wicket, wondering why on earth no one had as yet invented a more comfortable kind of pad.

The first ball he received was short-pitched, and he was able to deal with it in tennis fashion, swatting it to the mid-wicket boundary. He got no runs, but the crowd cheered.

The next ball took Uncle Ken on the pad. He was right in front of his wicket and should have been given out lbw. But the umpire hesitated to raise his finger. After all, hundreds of people had paid good money to see Bruce Hallam play, and it would have been a shame to disappoint them. 'Not out,' said the umpire.

The third ball took the edge of Uncle Ken's bat and sped through the slips.

'Lovely shot!' exclaimed an elderly gentleman in the pavilion.

'A classic late cut,' said another.

The ball reached the boundary and Uncle Ken had four runs to his name. Then it was 'over', and the other batsman had to face the bowling. He took a run off the first ball and called for a second run.

Uncle Ken thought one run was more than enough. Why go charging up and down the wicket like a mad man? However, he couldn't refuse to run, and he was halfway down the pitch when the fielder's throw hit the wicket. Uncle Ken was run-out by yards. There could be no doubt about it this time.

He returned to the pavilion to the sympathetic applause of the crowd.

'Not his fault,' said the elderly gentleman. 'The other chap shouldn't have called. There wasn't a run there. Still, it was worth coming here all the way from Kanpur if only to see that superb late cut . . .'

*

Uncle Ken enjoyed a hearty tiffin-lunch (taken at noon), and then, realizing that the Gomti team would probably have to be in the field for most of the afternoon—more running about!—he slipped out of the pavilion, left the stadium, and took a tonga to Aunt Emily's house in the cantonment.

He was just in time for a second lunch (taken at one o' clock) with Aunt Emily's family: and it was presumed at the stadium that Bruce Hallam had left early to catch the train to Allahabad, where he was expected to play in another charity match.

Aunt Emily, a forceful woman, fed Uncle Ken for a week, and then put him to work in the boys' dormitory of her school. It was several months before he was able to save up enough money to run away and return to Granny's place.

But he had the satisfaction of knowing that he had helped the great Bruce Hallam to add another four runs to his grand aggregate. The scorebook of the Gomti Cricketing Association had recorded his feat for all time:

'B. Hallam run-out 4.'

The Gomti team lost the match. But, as Uncle Ken would readily admit, where would we be without losers?

A Bicycle Ride with Uncle Ken

Kissing a girl while sharing a bicycle with her is no easy task, but I managed it when I was thirteen and my cousin Melanie was fourteen. Of course we both fell off in the process, and landed in one of Granny's flower beds where we were well cushioned by her nasturtiums.

I was a clumsy boy always falling off bicycles, and Cousin Melanie was teaching me to ride properly, making me sit on the front seat while she guided the infernal machine from the carrier seat. The kiss was purely experimental. I had not kissed a girl before, and as Cousin Melanie seemed eminently kissable, I thought I'd start with her. I waited until we were stationary, and she was instructing me on the intricacies of the cycle chain, and then I gave her a hurried kiss on the cheek. She was so startled that she fell backwards, taking me and the bicycle with her.

Later, she reported me to Granny, who said, 'We'll have to keep an eye on that boy. He's showing signs of a dissolute nature.'

'What's dissolute, Uncle Ken?' I asked my favourite uncle.

'It means you're going to the dogs. You're not supposed to kiss your cousin.'

'Can I kiss other girls?'

'Only if they are willing.'

'Did you ever kiss a girl, Uncle Ken?'

Uncle Ken blushed. 'Er . . . well . . . a long time ago.'

'Tell me about it.'

'Another time.'

'No, tell me now. How old were you?'

'About twenty.'

'And how old was she?'

'A bit younger.'

'And what happened?'

'We went cycling together. I was staying in Agra, when your grandfather worked there on the railways. Daisy's father was an engine-driver. But she didn't like engines; they left her covered with soot. Everyone had a bicycle in those days, only the very rich had cars. And the cars could not keep up with the bicycles.

'We lived in the cantonment, where the roads were straight and wide. Daisy and I went on cycle rides to Fatehpur Sikri and Secunderabad and of course the Taj Mahal, and one evening we saw the Taj Mahal by moonlight and it made us very romantic, and when I saw her home we kissed under the Asoka trees.'

'I didn't know you were so romantic, Uncle Ken. Why didn't you marry Daisy?'

'I didn't have a job. She said she'd wait until I got one, but after two years, she got tried of waiting. She married a ticket inspector.'

'Such a sad story,' I said. 'And you still don't have a job.'

Uncle Ken had been through various jobs—private tutor, salesman, shop assistant, hotel manager (until he brought about the closure of the hotel), and cricket coach, this last on the strength of bearing a close resemblance to Bruce Hallam—but at present he was unemployed, and only too ready to put his vast experience of life at my disposal.

Not only did he teach me to ride a bicycle but also accompanied me on cycle rides around Dehra and along the lanes and country roads outside the town.

A bicycle provides its rider with a great amount of freedom. A car will take you further but the fact that you're sitting in a confined space detracts from the freedom of the open spaces and unfamiliar roads. On a cycle you can feel the breeze on your face, smell the mango trees in blossom, slow down and gaze at the buffaloes wading in their ponds, or just stop anywhere and get down and enjoy a cup of tea or a glass of sugar cane juice. Foot-slogging takes time, and cars are too fast—everything whizzes past you before you can take a second look—and car drivers hate having to stop; they are intent only on reaching their destinations in good time. But a bicycle is just right for someone who likes to take a leisurely look at the world as well as to give the world a chance to look at him.

Uncle Ken and I had some exhilarating bicycle rides during my winter holidays, and the most memorable of these was our unplanned visit to a certain 'Rest Home' situated on the outskirts of the town. It isn't there now, so don't go looking for it.

We had cycled quite far that day, and were tired and thirsty. There was no sign of a tea shop on that particular road, but when we arrived at the open gate of an impressive building with a signboard saying 'Rest and Recuperation Centre', we presumed it was a hotel or hostelry of sorts and rode straight into the premises. There was an extensive lawn to one side, surrounded by neat hedges and flowering shrubs. A number of people were strolling about on the lawn; some were sitting on benches; one or two were straddling on a wall, talking to themselves; another was standing alone singing to a non-existent audience. Some were Europeans; a few were Indians.

We left our cycles in the porch and went in search of refreshment. A lady in a white sari gave us cool water from a surahi and told us we could wait on a bench just outside their office. But Uncle Ken said we'd prefer to meet some of the guests, and led me across the lawn to where the singer was practising his notes. He was a florid gentleman, heavily-built.

'Do you like my singing?' he asked, as we came up.

'Wonderful!' exclaimed Uncle Ken. 'You sing like Caruso.'

'I am Caruso!' affirmed the tenor, and let rip the opening notes of a famous operatic aria. 'Your tiny hand is frozen,' he sang, although it was an unusually warm day.

We hurried on, and met an elegant couple who were parading up and down the lawn, waving their hands to an invisible crowd.

'Good day to you, gentlemen,' said a flamboyant individual. 'You're the ambassadors from Sweden, I suppose.'

'If you so wish,' said Uncle Ken gallantly. 'And I have the honour of speaking to—?'

'The Emperor Napoleon, of course.'

'Of course. And this must be the Empress Josephine.' Uncle Ken bowed to the lady beside him.

'Actually, his Marie Waleska,' said Napoleon. 'Josephine is indisposed today.'

I was beginning to feel like Alice at the Mad Hatter's tea party, and began tugging at Uncle Ken's coat-sleeve, whispering that we were getting late for lunch.

A turbaned warrior with a tremendous moustache loomed in front of us. 'I'm Prithviraj Chauhan,' he announced. 'And I invite you to dinner at my palace.'

'Everyone's royalty here,' observed Uncle Ken.

'It's such a privilege to be with you.'

'Me too,' I put in nervously.

'Come with me, boy, and I'll introduce you to the others.' Prithviraj Chauhan took me by the hand and began guiding me across the lawn. 'There are many famous men and women here. That's Marco Polo over there. He's just back from China. And if you don't care for Caruso's signing, there's Tansen under

that tamarind tree. Tamarind leaves are good for the voice, you know that of course. And that fashionable gentleman there, he's Lord Curzon, who used to be a Viceroy. He's talking to the Sultan of Marrakesh. Come along, I'll introduce you to them . . . You're the young prince of Denmark, aren't you?'

'Hamlet himself,' said Uncle Ken with a wink.

Before I could refute any claims to royalty, we were intercepted by a white-coated gentleman accompanied by a white-coated assistant. They looked as though they were in charge.

'And what are you doing here, young man?' asked the senior of the two.

'I'm with my uncle,' I said, gesturing towards Uncle Ken, who approached and gave the in-charge an affable handshake.

'And you must be Dr Freud,' said Uncle Ken. 'I must say this is a jolly sort of place.'

'Actually, I'm Dr Goel. You must be the new patient we were expecting. But they should have sent you over with someone a little older than this boy. Never mind, come along to the office and we'll have you admitted.'

Uncle Ken and I both protested that we were not potential patients but had entered the grounds by mistake. We had our bicycles to prove it! But Dr Goel was having nothing of this deception. He and his assistant linked arms with Uncle Ken and marched him off to the office, while I trailed behind, wondering if I should get on my bicycle and rush back to Granny with the terrible news that Uncle Ken had been incarcerated in a lunatic asylum.

Just then an ambulance arrived with the real patient, a school principal suffering from a persecution complex. He kept shouting that he was perfectly sane, and that his entire staff had plotted to have him put away. This might well have been true, as the staff was there in force to make sure he did not escape.

Dr Goel apologized to Uncle Ken. Uncle Ken apologized to Dr Goel. The good doctor even accompanied us to the gate. He shook hands with Uncle Ken and said, 'I have a feeling we'll see you here again.' He looked hard at my uncle and added, 'I think I've seen you before, sir. What did you say your name was?'

'Bruce Hallam,' said Uncle Ken mischievously, and rode away before they changed their minds and kept him in their 'Rest Home'.

The Zigzag Walk

Uncle Ken always maintained that the best way to succeed in life was to zigzag. 'If you keep going off in new directions,' he declared, 'you will meet new career opportunities!'

Well, opportunities certainly came Uncle Ken's way, but he was not a success in the way that Dale Carnegie or Deepak Chopra would define a successful man . . .

In a long life devoted to 'muddling through' with the help of the family, Uncle Ken's many projects had included a chicken farm (rather like the one operated by Ukridge in Wodehouse's *Love Among the Chickens*) and a mineral water bottling project. For this latter enterprise, he bought a thousand soda water bottles and filled them with sulphur water from the springs five miles from Dehra. It was good stuff, taken in small quantities, but drunk one bottle at a time it proved corrosive—'sulphur and brimstone' as one irate customer described it—and angry buyers demonstrated in front of the house, throwing empty bottles over the wall into Grandmother's garden.

Grandmother was furious—more with Uncle Ken than with the demonstrators—and made him give everyone's money back.

'You have to be healthy and strong to take sulphur water,' he explained later.

'I thought it was supposed to make you healthy and strong,' I said.

Grandfather remarked that it did not compare with plain soda water, which he took with his whisky. 'Why don't you just bottle soda water?' he said. 'There's a much bigger demand for it.'

But Uncle Ken believed that he had to be original in all things.

'The secret to success is to zigzag,' he said.

'You certainly zigzagged round the garden when your customers were throwing their bottles back at you,' said Grandmother.

Uncle Ken also invented the zigzag walk.

The only way you could really come to know a place well was to walk in a truly haphazard way. To make a zigzag walk you take the first turning to the left, the first to the right, then the first to the left and so on. It can be quite fascinating, provided you are in no hurry to reach your destination. The trouble was that Uncle Ken used this zigzag method even when he had a train to catch.

When Grandmother asked him to go to the station to meet Aunt Mabel who was arriving from Simla, he zigzagged through town, taking in the botanical gardens in the west and the limestone factories to the east, finally reaching the station by way of the goods yard, in order, as he said, 'to take it by surprise'.

Nobody was surprised, least of all Aunt Mabel who had taken a tonga and reached the house while Uncle Ken was still sitting on the station platform, waiting for the next train to come in. I was sent to fetch him.

'Let's zigzag home again,' he said.

'Only on one condition, we eat chaat every fifteen minutes,' I said.

So we went home by way of all the most winding bazaars, and in north-Indian towns they do tend to zigzag, stopping at numerous chaat and halwai shops, until Uncle Ken had finished his money. We got home very late and were scolded by everyone; but as Uncle Ken told me, we were pioneers and had to expect to be misunderstood and even maligned. Posterity would recognize the true value of zigzagging.

'The zigzag way,' he said, 'is the diagonal between heart and reason.'

In our more troubled times, had he taken to preaching on the subject, he might have acquired a large following of dropouts. But Uncle Ken was the original dropout. He would not have tolerated others.

Had he been a space traveller he would have gone from star to star, zigzagging across the Milky Way.

Uncle Ken would not have succeeded in getting anywhere very fast, but I think he did succeed in getting at least one convert (myself) to see his point: 'When you zigzag, you are not choosing what to see in this world but you are giving the world a chance to see you!'

White Mice

Granny should never have entrusted my Uncle Ken with the job of taking me to the station and putting me on the train for Delhi. He got me to the station all right, but then proceeded to put me on the wrong train!

I was nine or ten at the time, and I'd been spending part of my winter holidays with my grandparents in Dehra. Now it was time to go back to my parents in Delhi, before joining school again.

'Just make sure that Ruskin gets into the right compartment,' said Gran to her only son Kenneth. 'And make sure he has a berth to himself and a thermos of drinking water.'

Uncle Ken carried out the instructions. He even bought me a bar of chocolate, consuming most of it himself while telling me how to pass my exams without too much study. (I'll tell you the secret some day.) The train pulled out of the station and we waved fond goodbyes to each other.

An hour and two small stations later, I discovered to my horror that I was not on the train to Delhi but on the night express to Lucknow, over 300 miles in the opposite direction. Someone in the compartment suggested that I get down at the next station; another said it would not be wise for a small boy to get off the train at a strange place in the middle of the night. 'Wait till we get to Lucknow,' advised another passenger, 'then send a telegram to your parents.'

Early next morning the train steamed into Lucknow. One of the passengers kindly took me to the stationmaster's office. 'Mr P.K. Ghosh, Stationmaster,' said the sign over his door. When my predicament had been explained to him, Mr Ghosh looked down at me through his bifocals and said, 'Yes, yes, we must send a telegram to your parents.'

'I don't have their address as yet,' I said. 'They were to meet me in Delhi. You'd better send a telegram to my grandfather in Dehra.'

'Done, done,' said Mr Ghosh, who was in the habit of repeating certain words. 'And meanwhile, I'll take you home and introduce you to my family.'

Mr Ghosh's house was just behind the station. He had his cook bring me a cup of sweet milky tea and two large rasgullas, syrupy Indian sweetmeats.

'You like rasgullas, I hope, I hope?'

'Oh yes, sir,' I said. 'Thank you very much.'

'Now let me show you my family.'

And he took me by the hand and led me to a boarded-up veranda at the back of the house. Here I was amazed to find a miniature railway, complete with a station, railway bungalows, signal boxes, and next to it a miniature fairground complete with swings, roundabout and a ferris wheel. Cavorting on the roundabout and ferris wheel were some fifteen to twenty white mice! Another dozen or so ran in and out of tunnels, and climbed up on a toy train. Mr Ghosh pressed a button and the little train, crowded with white mice, left the station and went rattling off to the far corner of the veranda.

'My hobby for many years,' said Mr Ghosh. 'What do you think of it—think of it?'

'I like the train, sir.'

'But not the mice?'

'There are an awful lot of them, sir. They must consume a great many rasgullas!'

'No, no, I don't give them rasgullas,' snapped Mr

Ghosh, a little annoyed. 'Just railway biscuits, broken up. These old station biscuits are just the thing for them. Some of our biscuits haven't been touched for years. Too hard for our teeth. Rasgullas are for you and me! Now I'll leave you here while I return to the office and send a telegram to your grandfather. These new-fangled telephones never work properly!'

*

Grandfather arrived that evening, and in the meantime I helped feed the white mice with railways biscuits, then watched Mr Ghosh operate the toy train. Some of the mice took the train, some played on the swings and roundabouts, while some climbed in and out of Mr Ghosh's pockets and ran up and down his uniform. By the time Grandfather arrived, I had consumed about a dozen rasgullas and fallen asleep in a huge railway armchair in Mr Ghosh's living room. I woke up to find the stationmaster busy showing Grandfather his little railway colony of white mice. Grandfather, being a retired railwayman, was more interested in the toy train, but he said polite things about the mice, commending their pink eyes and pretty little feet. Mr Ghosh beamed with pleasure and sent out for more rasgullas.

When Grandfather and I had settled into the compartment of a normal train late that night, Mr Ghosh came to the window to say goodbye.

As the train began moving, he thrust a cardboard box into my hands and said, 'A present for you and your grandfather!'

'More rasgullas,' I thought. But when the train was underway and I had lifted the lid of the box, I found two white mice asleep on a bed of cotton wool.

*

Back in Dehra, I kept the white mice in their box; I had plans for them. Uncle Ken had spent most of the day skulking in the guava orchard, too embarrassed to face me. Granny had given him a good lecture on how to be a responsible adult. But I was thirsty for revenge!

After dinner I slipped into my uncle's room and released the mice under his bed-sheet.

An hour later we had all to leap out of our beds when Uncle Ken dashed out of his room, screaming that something soft and furry was running about inside his pyjamas.

'Well, off with the pyjamas!' said Grandfather, giving me a wink; he had a good idea of what had happened.

After Uncle Ken had done a tap dance, one white mouse finally emerged from the pyjamas; but the other had run up the sleeve of his pyjama-coat and suddenly popped out beneath my uncle's chin. Uncle Ken grew hysterical. Convinced that his room was full of mice—pink, white and brown—he locked himself into the storeroom and slept on an old sofa.

Next day Grandfather took me to the station and put me on the train to Delhi. It was the right train this time.

'I'll look after the white mice,' he said.

Grandfather grew quite fond of the mice, and even wrote to Mr Ghosh, asking if he could spare another pair. But Mr Ghosh, he learnt later, had been transferred to another part of the country, and had taken his family with him.

The Ghost Who Got In

It was Grandfather who finally decided that we would have to move to another house.

And it was all because of a *Pret*, a mischievous north-Indian ghost, who had been making life difficult for everyone.

Prets usually live in peepal trees, and that's where our little ghost first had his abode—in the branches of a massive old peepal tree which had grown through the compound wall and spread into our garden. Part of the tree was on our side of the wall, part on the other side, shading the main road. It gave the ghost a commanding view of the entire area.

For many years the Pret had lived there quite happily, without bothering anyone in our house. It did not bother me, either, and I spent a lot of time in the peepal tree. Sometimes I went there to escape the adults at home, sometimes to watch the road and people who passed by. The peepal tree was cool on a hot day, and the heart-shaped leaves were always revolving in the breeze. This constant movement of the leaves also helped to disguise the movements of the Pret, so that I never really knew exactly where he was sitting. But he paid no attention to me. The traffic on the road kept him fully occupied.

Sometimes, when a tonga was passing, he would jump down and frighten the pony, and as a result the little pony cart would go rushing off in the wrong direction.

Sometimes he would get into the engine of a car or a bus, which would have a breakdown soon afterwards.

And he liked to knock the sola-topees (pith helmets) off the heads of sahibs or officials, who would wonder how a strong breeze had sprung up so suddenly, only to die down just as quickly. Although this special kind of ghost could make himself felt, and sometimes heard, he was invisible to the human eye.

I was not invisible to the human eye, and often got the blame for some of the Pret's pranks. If bicycle riders were struck by mango seeds or apricot stones, they would look up, see a small boy in the branches of the tree, and threaten me with dire consequences.

Drivers who went off after parking their cars in the shade would sometimes come back to find their tyres flat. My protests of innocence did not carry much weight. But when I mentioned the Pret in the tree, they would look uneasy, either because they thought I must be mad, or because they were afraid of ghosts, especially Prets. They would find other things to do and hurry away.

At night no one walked beneath the peepal tree.

It was said that if you yawned beneath the tree, the Pret would jump down your throat and ruin your digestion. Our gardener, Chandu, who was always taking sick leave, blamed the Pret for his tummy troubles. Once, when yawning, Chandu had forgotten to snap his fingers in front of his mouth, and the ghost had got in without any trouble.

Now Chandu spent most of his time lying on a string-bed in the courtyard of his small house. When Grandmother went to visit him, he would start groaning and holding his sides, the pain was so bad; but when she went away, he did not fuss so much. He claimed that the pain did not affect his appetite, and he ate a normal diet, in fact a little more than normal—the extra amount was meant to keep the ghost happy!

'Well, it isn't our fault,' said Grandfather, who had given permission to the Public Works Department to cut the tree, which had been on our land. They wanted to widen the road, and the tree and a bit of our wall were in the way. So both had to go.

Several people protested, including the Maharaja of Jetpur, who lived across the road and who sometimes asked Grandfather over for a game of tennis.

'That peepal tree has been there for hundreds of years,' he said. 'Who are we to cut it down?'

'*We*,' said the Chief Engineer, 'are the P.W.D.'

And not even a ghost can prevail against the wishes of the Public Works Department.

They brought men with saws and axes, and first they lopped all the branches until the poor tree was quite naked. (It must have been at this moment that the Pret moved out.) Then they sawed away at the trunk until, finally, the great old peepal came crashing down on the road, bringing down the telephone wires and an electric pole in the process, and knocking a large gap in the Maharaja's garden wall.

It took them three days to clear the road, and during that time the Chief Engineer swallowed a lot of dust and tree pollen. For months afterwards he complained of a choking feeling, although no doctor could ever find anything in his throat.

'It's the Pret's doing,' said the Maharaja knowingly. 'They should never have cut that tree.'

Deprived of his tree, the Pret decided that he would live in our house.

I first became aware of his presence when I was sitting on the veranda steps, reading a novel. A tiny chuckling sound came from behind me. I looked around, but no one was to be seen. When I returned to my book, the chuckling started again. I paid no attention. Then a shower of rose petals fell softly on to the pages of my open book. The Pret wanted me to know he was there!

'All right,' I said. 'So you've come to stay with us. Now let me read.'

He went away then; but as a good Pret has to be bad in order to justify his existence, it was not long before he was up to all sorts of mischief.

He began by hiding Grandmother's spectacles.

'I'm sure I put them down on the dining table,' she grumbled.

A little later they were found balanced on the snout of a wild boar, whose stuffed and mounted head adorned the veranda wall, a memento of

Grandfather's youthful hunting exploits. Naturally, I was at first blamed for this prank. But a day or two later, when the spectacles disappeared again, only to be found dangling from the bars of the parrot's cage, it was agreed that I was not to blame; for the parrot had once bitten off a piece of my finger, and I did not go near it any more.

The parrot was hanging upside down, trying to peer through one of the lenses. I don't know if they improved his vision, but what he saw certainly made him angry, because the pupils of his eyes went very small and he dug his beak into the spectacle frames, leaving them with a permanent dent. I caught them just before they fell to the floor.

Our parrot must have been psychic, because even without the help of the spectacles it seemed that he could see the Pret. He would keep turning this way and that, lunging out at unseen fingers, and protecting his tail from the tweaks of invisible hands. He had always refused to learn to talk, but now he became quite voluble and began to chatter in some unknown tongue, often screaming with rage and rolling his eyes in a frenzy.

'We'll have to give that parrot away,' said

Grandmother. 'He gets more bad-tempered by the day.'

Grandfather was the next to be troubled.

He went into the garden one morning to find all his prize sweet peas broken off and lying on the grass. Chandu thought the sparrows had destroyed the flowers, but we didn't think the birds could have finished off every single bloom just before sunrise.

'It must be the Pret,' said Grandfather, and I agreed.

The Pret did not trouble me much, because he remembered me from his peepal tree days and knew I resented the tree being cut as much as he did. But he liked to catch my attention, and he did this by chuckling and squeaking near me when I was alone, or whispering in my ear when I was with someone else. Gradually I began to make out the occasional word. He had started learning English!

Uncle Ken, who came to stay with us for long periods when he had little else to do (which was most of the time), was soon to suffer.

He was a heavy sleeper, and once he'd gone to bed he hated being woken up. So when he came to breakfast looking bleary-eyed and miserable, we asked him if he was feeling all right.

'I couldn't sleep a wink last night,' he complained. 'Whenever I was about to fall asleep, the bedclothes would be pulled off the bed. I had to get up at least a dozen times to pick them off the floor.' He stared suspiciously at me. 'Where were *you* sleeping last night, young man?'

'In Grandfather's room,' I said. 'I've lent you *my* room.'

'It's that ghost from the peepal tree,' said Grandmother with a sigh.

'Ghost!' exclaimed Uncle Ken. 'I didn't know the house was haunted.'

'It is now,' said Grandmother. 'First my spectacles, then the sweet peas, and now Ken's bedclothes! What will it to be up to next, I wonder?'

We did not have to wonder for long.

There followed a series of minor disasters. Vases fell off tables, pictures fell from walls. Parrots' feathers turned up in the teapot, while the parrot himself let out indignant squawks and swear words in the middle of the night. Windows which had been closed would be found open, and open windows closed.

Finally, Uncle Ken found a crow's nest in his bed, and on tossing it out of the window was attacked by two crows.

Then Aunt Ruby came to stay, and things quietened down for a time.

Did Aunt Ruby's powerful personality have an effect on the Pret, or was he just sizing her up?

'I think the Pret has taken a fancy to your aunt,' said Grandfather mischievously. 'He's behaving himself for a change.'

This may have been true, because the parrot, who had picked up some of the English words being tried out by the Pret, now called out 'Kiss, kiss' whenever Aunt Ruby was in the room.

'What a charming bird,' said Aunt Ruby.

'You can keep him if you like,' said Grandmother.

One day Aunt Ruby came into the house covered in rose petals.

'I don't know where they came from,' she exclaimed. 'I was sitting in the garden, drying my hair, when handfuls of petals came showering down on me!'

'It likes you,' said Grandmother.

'What likes me?'

'The ghost.'

'What ghost?'

'The Pret. It came to live in the house when the peepal tree was cut down.'

'What nonsense!' said Aunt Ruby.

'Kiss, kiss!' screamed the parrot.

'There aren't any ghosts, Prets or other kinds,' said Aunt Ruby firmly.

'Kiss, kiss!' screeched the parrot again. Or was it the parrot? The sound seemed to be coming from the ceiling.

'I wish that parrot would shut up.'

'It isn't the parrot,' I said. 'It's the Pret.'

Aunt Ruby gave me a cuff over the ear and stormed out of the room.

But she had offended the Pret. From being her admirer he turned into her enemy. Somehow her toothpaste got switched with a tube of Grandfather's shaving cream. When she appeared in the dining room, foaming at the mouth, we ran for our lives, Uncle Ken shouting that she'd got rabies.

Two days later Aunt Ruby complained that she had been struck on the nose by a grapefruit, which had leapt mysteriously from the pantry shelf and hurled itself at her.

'If Ruby and Ken stay here much longer, they'll both have nervous breakdowns,' said Grandfather thoughtfully.

'I thought they broke down long ago,' I said.

'None of your cheek,' snapped Aunt Ruby.

'He's in league with that Pret to try and get us out of here,' said Uncle Ken.

'Don't listen to him—you can stay as long as you like,' said Grandmother.

The Pret, however, did not feel so hospitable, and the persecution of Aunt Ruby continued.

'When I looked in the mirror this morning,' she complained bitterly, 'I saw a little monster, with huge ears, bulging eyes, flaring nostrils and a toothless grin!'

'You don't look that bad, Aunt Ruby,' I said trying to be nice.

'It was either you or that imp you call a Pret,' said Aunt Ruby. 'And if it's a ghost, then it's time we all moved to another house.'

Uncle Ken had another idea.

'Let's drive the ghost out,' he said. 'I know a sadhu who rids houses of evil spirits.'

'But the Pret's not evil,' I said. 'Just mischievous.'

Uncle Ken went off to the bazaar and came back a few hours later with a scruffy-looking sadhu—a sadhu being a man who is supposed to have given up all worldly goods, including most of his clothes.

The sadhu prowled about the house and lighted incense in all the rooms, despite squawks of protest from the parrot. All the time he chanted various magic spells. He then collected a fee of thirty rupees and promised that we would not be bothered again by the Pret.

As he was leaving, he was suddenly blessed with a shower—no, it was really a downpour—of dead flowers, decaying leaves, orange peels and banana skins. All spells forgotten, he ran to the gate and made for the safety of the bazaar.

Aunt Ruby declared that it had become impossible to sleep at night because of the devilish chuckling that came from beneath her pillow. She packed her bags and left.

Uncle Ken stayed on. He was still having trouble with his bedclothes, and he was beginning to talk to himself, which was a bad sign.

One day I found him on the drawing room sofa, laughing like a mad man. Even the parrot was so alarmed that it was silent, head lowered and curious. Uncle Ken was red in the face—literally red all over!

'What happened to your face, Uncle?' I asked.

He stopped laughing and gave me a long, hard look. I realized that there had been no joy in his laughter.

'Who painted the washbasin red without telling me?' he asked in a quavering voice.

'We'll have to move, I suppose,' said Grandfather later. 'Even if it's only for a couple of months. I'm worried about Ken. I've told him that I painted the washbasin myself but forgot to tell him. He doesn't believe me. He thinks it's the Pret or the boy, or both of them! Ken needs a change. So do we. There's my brother's house at the other end of the town. He won't be using it for a few months. We'll move in next week.'

And so, a few days and several disasters later, we began moving house.

*

Two bullock carts laden with furniture and heavy luggage were sent ahead. Uncle Ken went with them. The roof of our old car was piled high with bags and kitchen utensils. Grandfather took the wheel, I sat beside him, and Granny sat in state at the back.

We started off and had gone some way down the main road when Grandfather started having trouble with the steering wheel. It appeared to have got loose, and the car began veering about on the road, scattering cyclists, pedestrians and stray dogs, pigs and hens. A stray cow refused to move, but we missed it somehow, and then suddenly we were off the road and making for a low wall.

Grandfather pressed his foot down on the brake, but we only went faster. 'Watch out!' he shouted.

It was the Maharaja of Jetpur's garden wall made of single bricks, and the car knocked it down quite easily and went on through it, coming to a stop on the Maharaja's lawn.

'Now look what you've done,' said Grandmother.

'Well, we missed the flower beds,' said Grandfather. 'Someone's been tinkering with the car. Our Pret, no doubt.'

The Maharaja and two attendants came running towards us.

The Maharaja was a perfect gentleman, and when he saw that the driver was Grandfather, he beamed with pleasure.

'Delighted to see you, old chap!' he exclaimed. 'Jolly decent of you to drop in. How about a game of tennis?'

'Sorry to have come in through the wall,' apologized Grandfather.

'Don't mention it, old chap. The gate was closed, so what else could you do?'

Grandfather was as much of a gentleman as the Maharaja, so he thought it only fair to join him in a game of tennis. Grandmother and I watched and drank lemonades. After the game, the Maharaja waved us goodbye and we drove back through the hole in the wall and out on to the road. There was nothing much wrong with the car.

We hadn't gone far when we heard a peculiar sound, as if someone was chuckling and talking to himself. It came from the roof of the car.

'Is the parrot out there on the luggage-rack?' asked Grandfather.

'No,' said Grandmother. 'He went ahead with Ken.'

Grandfather stopped the car, got out, and examined the roof.

'Nothing up there,' he said, getting in again and starting the engine. 'I thought I heard the parrot.'

When we had gone a little further, the chuckling started again. A squeaky little voice began talking in English in the tones of the parrot.

'It's the Pret,' whispered Grandmother. 'What is he saying?'

The Pret's squawk grew louder. 'Come on, come on!' he cried gleefully. 'A new house! The same old friends! What fun we're going to have!'

Grandfather stopped the car. He backed into a driveway, turned round, and began driving back to the old house.

'What are you doing?' asked Grandfather.

'Going home,' said Grandfather.

'And what about the Pret?'

'What about him? He's decided to live with us so we'll have to make the best of it. You can't solve a problem by running away from it.'

'All right,' said Granny. 'But what will we do about Ken?'

'It's up to him, isn't it? He'll be all right if he finds something to do.'

Grandfather stopped the car in front of the veranda steps.

'I'm hungry,' I said.

'It will have to be a picnic lunch,' said Grandmother. 'Almost everything was sent off on the bullock carts.'

As we got out of the car and climbed the veranda steps, we were greeted by showers of rose petals and sweet-scented jasmine.

'How lovely!' exclaimed Grandmother, smiling. 'I think he likes us, after all.'

Monkey Trouble

Grandfather bought Tutu from a street entertainer for a sum of ten rupees. The man had three monkeys. Tutu was the smallest, but the most mischievous. She was tied up most of the time. The little monkey looked so miserable with a collar and chain that Grandfather decided it would be much happier in our home. Grandfather had a weakness for keeping unusual pets. It was a habit that I, at the age of eight or nine, used to encourage.

Grandmother at first objected to having a monkey in the house. 'You have enough pets as it is,' she said, referring to Grandfather's goat, several white mice, and a small tortoise.

'But I don't have any,' I said.

'You're wicked enough for two monkeys. One boy in the house is all I can take.'

'Ah, but Tutu isn't a boy,' said Grandfather triumphantly. 'This is a little girl monkey!'

Grandmother gave in. She had always wanted a little girl in the house. She believed girls were less troublesome than boys. Tutu was to prove her wrong.

She was a pretty little monkey. Her bright eyes sparkled with mischief beneath deep-set eyebrows. And her teeth, which were a pearly white, were often revealed in a grin that frightened the wits out of Aunt Ruby, whose nerves had already suffered from the presence of Grandfather's pet python in the house at Lucknow. But this was Dehra, my grandparents' house, and aunts and uncles had to put up with our pets.

Tutu's hands had a dried-up look, as though they had been pickled in the sun for many years. One of the first things I taught her was to shake hands, and this she insisted on doing with all who visited the house. Peppery Major Malik would have to stoop and shake hands with Tutu before he could enter the drawing room, otherwise Tutu would climb on to his shoulder and stay there, roughing up his hair and playing with his moustache.

Uncle Ken couldn't stand any of our pets and took a particular dislike to Tutu, who was always making faces at him. But as Uncle Ken was never in a job for long, and depended on Grandfather's good-natured generosity, he had to shake hands with Tutu, like everyone else.

Tutu's fingers were quick and wicked. And her tail, while adding to her good looks (Grandfather believed a tail would add to anyone's good looks!) also served as a third hand. She could use it to hang from a branch, and it was capable of scooping up any delicacy that might be out of reach of her hands.

Aunt Ruby had not been informed of Tutu's arrival. Loud shrieks from her bedroom brought us running to see what was wrong. It was only Tutu trying on Aunt Ruby's petticoats! They were much too large, of course, and when Aunt Ruby entered the room, all she saw was a faceless white blob jumping up and down on the bed.

We disentangled Tutu and soothed Aunt Ruby. I gave Tutu a bunch of sweet peas to make her happy. Granny didn't like anyone plucking her sweet peas, so I took some from Major Malik's garden while he was having his afternoon siesta.

Then Uncle Ken complained that his hairbrush was missing. We found Tutu sunning herself on the back veranda, using the hairbrush to scratch her armpits.

I took it from her and handed it back to Uncle Ken with an apology; but he flung the brush away with an oath.

'Such a fuss about nothing,' I said. 'Tutu doesn't have fleas!'

'No, and she bathes more often than Ken,' said Grandfather, who had borrowed Aunt Ruby's shampoo to give Tutu a bath.

All the same, Grandmother objected to Tutu being given the run of the house. Tutu had to spend her nights in the outhouse, in the company of the goat. They got on quite well, and it was not long before Tutu was seen sitting comfortably on the back of the goat, while the goat roamed the back garden in search of its favourite grass.

The day Grandfather had to visit Meerut to collect his railway pension, he decided to take Tutu and me along to keep us both out of mischief, he said. To prevent Tutu from wandering about on the train, causing inconvenience to passengers, she was provided with a large black travelling bag. This, with some straw at the bottom, became her compartment. Grandfather and I paid for our seats, and we took Tutu along as hand baggage.

There was enough space for Tutu to look out of

the bag occasionally, and to be fed with bananas and biscuits, but she could not get her hands through the opening and the canvas was too strong for her to bite her way through.

Tutu's efforts to get out only had the effect of making the bag roll about on the floor or occasionally jump into the air—an exhibition that attracted a curious crowd of onlookers at the Dehra and Meerut railway stations.

Anyway, Tutu remained in the bag as far as Meerut, but while Grandfather was producing our tickets at the turnstile, she suddenly poked her head out of the bag and gave the ticket collector a wide grin.

The poor man was taken aback. But, with great presence of mind and much to Grandfather's annoyance, he said, 'Sir, you have a dog with you. You'll have to buy a ticket for it.'

'It's not a dog!' said Grandfather indignantly. 'This is a baby monkey of the species *macacus-mischievous*, closely related to the human species *homus-horriblis!* And there is no charge for babies.'

'It's as big as a cat,' said the ticket collector. 'Cats and dogs have to be paid for.'

'But, I tell you, it's only a baby,' protested Grandfather.

'Have you a birth certificate to prove that?' demanded the ticket collector.

'Next, you'll be asking to see her mother,' snapped Grandfather.

In vain did he take Tutu out of the bag. In vain did he try to prove that a young monkey did not qualify as a dog or a cat or even as a quadruped. Tutu was classified as a dog by the ticket collector, and five rupees were handed over as her fare.

Then Grandfather, just to get his own back, took from his pocket the small tortoise that he sometimes carried about, and said: 'And what must I pay for this, since you charge for all creatures great and small?'

The ticket collector looked closely at the tortoise, prodded it with his forefinger, gave Grandfather a triumphant look, and said, 'No charge, sir. It is not a dog!'

*

Winters in north India can be very cold. A great treat for Tutu on winter evenings was the large bowl of hot water given to her by Grandfather for a bath. Tutu would cunningly test the temperature with her hand, then gradually step into the bath, first one foot, then the other (as she had seen me doing) until she was in the water up to her neck.

Once comfortable, she would take the soap in her hands or feet and rub herself all over. When the water became cold, she would get out and run as quickly as she could to the kitchen fire in order to dry herself. If anyone laughed at her during this performance, Tutu's feelings would be hurt and she would refuse to go on with the bath.

*

One day Tutu almost succeeded in boiling herself alive. Grandmother had left a large kettle on the fire for tea. And Tutu, all by herself and with nothing better to do, decided to remove the lid. Finding the water just warm enough for a bath, she got in, with her head sticking out from the open kettle.

This was fine for a while, until the water began to get heated. Tutu raised herself a little. But finding it cold outside, she sat down again. She continued hopping up and down for some time, until Grandfather returned and hauled her, half-boiled, out of the kettle.

'What's for tea today?' asked Uncle Ken gleefully. 'Boiled eggs and a half-boiled monkey?'

But Tutu was none the worse for the adventure and continued to bathe more regularly than Uncle Ken.

Aunt Ruby was a frequent taker of baths. This met with Tutu's approval—so much so that, one day, when Aunt Ruby had finished shampooing her hair, she looked up through a lather of bubbles and soap-suds to see Tutu sitting opposite her in the bath, following her example.

One day Aunt Ruby took us all by surprise. She announced that she had become engaged. We had always thought Aunt Ruby would never marry—she had often said so herself—but it appeared that the right man had now come along in the person of Rocky Fernandes, a schoolteacher from Goa.

Rocky was a tall, firm-jawed, good-natured man, a couple of years younger than Aunt Ruby. He had a fine baritone voice and sang in the manner of the great Nelson Eddy. As Grandmother liked baritone singers, Rocky was soon in her good books.

'But what on earth does he see in her?' Uncle Ken wanted to know.

'More than any girl has seen in you!' snapped Grandmother. 'Ruby's a fine girl. And they're both teachers. Maybe they can start a school of their own.'

Rocky visited the house quite often and brought

me chocolates and cashewnuts, of which he seemed to have an unlimited supply. He also taught me several marching songs. Naturally, I approved of Rocky. Aunt Ruby won my grudging admiration for having made such a wise choice.

One day I overheard them talking of going to the bazaar to buy an engagement ring. I decided I would go along too. But as Aunt Ruby had made it clear that she did not want me around, I decided that I had better follow at a discreet distance. Tutu, becoming aware that a mission of some importance was under way, decided to follow me. But as I had not invited her along, she too decided to keep out of sight.

Once in the crowded bazaar, I was able to get quite close to Aunt Ruby and Rocky without being spotted. I waited until they had settled down in a large jewellery shop before sauntering past and spotting them, as though by accident. Aunt Ruby wasn't too pleased at seeing me, but Rocky waved and called out, 'Come and join us! Help your aunt choose a beautiful ring!'

The whole thing seemed to be a waste of good money, but I did not say so—Aunt Ruby was giving me one of her more unloving looks.

'Look, these are pretty!' I said, pointing to some cheap, bright agates set in white metal. But Aunt

Ruby wasn't looking. She was immersed in a case of diamonds.

'Why not a ruby for Aunt Ruby?' I suggested, trying to please her.

'That's her lucky stone,' said Rocky. 'Diamonds are the thing for engagements.' And he started singing a song about a diamond being a girl's best friend.

While the jeweller and Aunt Ruby were sifting through the diamond rings, and Rocky was trying out another tune, Tutu had slipped into the shop without being noticed by anyone but me. A little sequeal of delight was the first sign she gave of her presence. Everyone looked up to see her trying on a pretty necklace.

'And what are those stones?' I asked.

'They look like pearls,' said Rocky.

'They are pearls,' said the shopkeeper, making a grab for them.

'It's that dreadful monkey!' cried Aunt Ruby. 'I knew that boy would bring him here!'

The necklace was already adorning Tutu's neck. I thought she looked rather nice in them, but she gave us no time to admire the effect. Springing out of our reach, Tutu dodged around Rocky, slipped between my legs, and made for the crowded road.

I ran after her, shouting to her to stop, but she wasn't listening.

There were no branches to assist Tutu in her progress, but she used the heads and shoulders of people as springboards and so made rapid headway through the bazaar.

The jeweller left his shop and ran after us. So did Rocky. So did several bystanders, who had seen the incident. And others, who had no idea what it was all about, joined in the chase. As Grandfather used to say, 'In a crowd, everyone plays follow-the-leader, even when they don't know who's leading.' Not everyone knew that the leader was Tutu. Only the front runners could see her.

She tried to make her escape speedier by leaping on to the back of a passing scooterist. The scooter swerved into a fruit stall and came to a standstill under a heap of bananas, while the scooterist found himself in the arms of an indignant fruitseller. Tutu peeled a banana and ate part of it, before deciding to move on.

From an awning she made an emergency landing on a washerman's donkey. The donkey promptly panicked and rushed down the road, while bundles of washing fell by the wayside. The washerman joined in the chase. Children on their way to school decided that here was something better to do than attend classes. With shouts of glee, they soon overtook their panting elders.

Tutu finally left the bazaar and took a road leading in the direction of our house. But knowing that she would be caught and locked up once she got home, she decided to end the chase by ridding herself of the necklace. Deftly removing it from her neck, she flung it in the small canal that ran down the road.

The jeweller, with a cry of anguish, plunged into the canal. So did Rocky. So did I. So did several other people, both adults and children. It was to be a treasure hunt!

Some twenty minutes later, Rocky shouted, 'I've found it!' Covered in mud, water lilies, ferns and tadpoles, we emerged from the canal, and Rocky presented the necklace to the relieved shopkeeper.

Everyone trudged back to the bazaar to find Aunt Ruby waiting in the shop, still trying to make up her mind about a suitable engagement ring.

Finally the ring was bought, the engagement was announced, and a date was set for the wedding.

'I don't want that monkey anywhere near us on our wedding day,' declared Aunt Ruby.

'We'll lock her up in the outhouse,' promised Grandfather. 'And we'll let her out only after you've left for your honeymoon.'

A few days before the wedding I found Tutu in the kitchen, helping Grandmother prepare the wedding cake. Tutu often helped with the cooking and, when Grandmother wasn't looking, added herbs, spices, and other interesting items to the pots—so that occasionally we found a chilli in the custard or an onion in the jelly or a strawberry floating in the chicken soup.

Sometimes these additions improved a dish, sometimes they did not. Uncle Ken lost a tooth when he bit firmly into a sandwich which contained walnut shells.

I'm not sure exactly what went into that wedding cake when Grandmother wasn't looking—she insisted that Tutu was always very well behaved in the kitchen—but I did spot Tutu stirring in some red chilli sauce, bitter gourd seeds, and a generous helping of eggshells!

It's true that some of the guests were not seen for several days after the wedding, but no one said anything against the cake. Most people thought it had an interesting flavour.

The great day dawned, and the wedding guests made their way to the little church that stood on the outskirts of Dehra—a town with a church, two mosques, and several temples.

I had offered to dress Tutu up as a bridesmaid and bring her along, but no one except Grandfather thought it was a good idea. So I was an obedient boy and locked Tutu in the outhouse. I did, however, leave the skylight open a little. Grandmother had always said that fresh air was good for growing children, and I thought Tutu should have her share of it.

The wedding ceremony went without a hitch. Aunt Ruby looked a picture, and Rocky looked like a film star.

Grandfather played the organ, and did so with such gusto that the small choir could hardly be heard. Grandmother cried a little, I sat quietly in a corner, with the little tortoise on my lap.

When the service was over, we trooped out into the sunshine and made our way back to the house for the reception.

The feast had been laid out on tables in the garden. As the gardener had been left in charge, everything was in order. Tutu was on her best behaviour. She had, it appeared, used the skylight to avail of more fresh air outside, and now sat beside the three-tier wedding cake, guarding it against crows, squirrels and the goat. She greeted the guests with squeals of delight.

It was too much for Aunt Ruby. She flew at Tutu in a rage. And Tutu, sensing that she was not welcome, leapt away, taking with her the top tier of the wedding cake.

Led by Major Malik, we followed her into the orchard, only to find that she had climbed to the top of the jackfruit tree. From there she proceeded to pelt us with bits of wedding cake. She had also managed to get hold of a bag of confetti, and when she ran out of cake she showered us with confetti.

'That's more like it!' said the good-humoured Rocky. 'Now let's return to the party, folks!'

Uncle Ken remained with Major Malik, determined to chase Tutu away. He kept throwing stones into the tree, until he received a large piece of cake bang on his nose. Muttering threats, he returned to the party, leaving the Major to do the battle.

When the festivities were finally over, Uncle Ken took the old car out of the garage and drove up the veranda steps. He was going to drive Aunt Ruby and Rocky to the nearby hill resort of Mussoorie, where they would have their honeymoon.

Watched by family and friends, Aunt Ruby climbed into the back seat. She waved regally to everyone. She leant out of the window and offered me her cheek and I had to kiss her farewell. Everyone wished them luck.

As Rocky burst into song, Uncle Ken opened the throttle and stepped on the accelerator. The car shot forward in a cloud of dust.

Rocky and Aunt Ruby continued to wave to us. And so did Tutu, from her perch on the rear bumper! She was clutching a bag in her hands and showering confetti on all who stood in the driveway.

'They don't know Tutu's with them!' I exclaimed.

'She'll go all the way to Mussoorie! Will Aunt Ruby let her stay with them?'

'Tutu might ruin the honeymoon,' said Grandfather. 'But don't worry—our Ken will bring her back!'

Uncle Ken's Feathered Foes

Uncle Ken looked smug and pleased with life. He had just taken a large bite out of a currant bun (well buttered inside, with strawberry jam as a stuffing) and was about to take a second bite when, out of a clear blue sky, a hawk swooped down, snatched the bun out of Uncle Ken's hands and flew away with its trophy.

It was a bad time for Uncle Ken. He was being persecuted—not by his sisters or the world at large, but by the birds in our compound.

It all began when he fired his air gun at a noisy bunch of crows, and one of them fell dead on the veranda steps.

The crows never forgave him.

He had only to emerge from the house for a few minutes, and they would fling themselves at him, a noisy gang of ten to fifteen crows, swooping down with flapping wings and extended beaks, knocking off his hat and clawing at his flailing arms. If Uncle Ken wanted to leave the compound, he would have to sneak out of the back veranda, make a dash for his bicycle, and pedal furiously down the driveway until he was out of the gate and on the main road. Even then, he would be pursued by two or three outraged crows until he was well outside their territory.

This persecution continued for two or three weeks, until, in desperation, Uncle Ken adopted a disguise. He put on a false beard, a deer-stalker cap (in the manner of Sherlock Holmes), a long black cloak (in the manner of Count Dracula), and a pair of Grandfather's old riding boots. And so attired, he marched up and down the driveway, frightening away two elderly ladies who had come to see Grandmother. The crows were suitably baffled and kept at a distance. But Granny's pet mongrel, Crazy, began barking furiously, caught hold of Uncle Ken's cloak and wouldn't let go until I came to his rescue.

*

The mango season was approaching, and we were all looking forward to feasting on our mangoes that summer.

There were three or four mango trees in our compound, and Uncle Ken was particularly anxious to protect them from monkeys, parrots, flying foxes and other fruit-eating creatures. He had his own favourite mango tree, and every afternoon he would place a cot beneath it, and whenever he spotted winged or furred intruders in the tree, he would put a small bugle to his lips and produce a shrill bugle call—loud enough to startle everyone in the house as well as the denizens of the trees.

However, after a few shattering bugle calls Uncle Ken would doze off, only to wake up an hour later bespattered with the droppings of parrots, pigeons, squirrels, and other inhabitants of the mango tree. After two or three days of blessings from the birds, Uncle Ken came out with a large garden umbrella which protected him from aerial bombardment.

While he was fast asleep one afternoon (after spoiling Grandfather's siesta with his horn blowing), Granny caught me by the hand and said, 'Be a good boy; go out and fetch that bugle.'

I did as I was told, slipping the bugle out of Uncle Ken's hands as he snored, and handing it over to Granny. I'm not sure what she did with it, but a few weeks later, as a wedding band came down the road, drums beating and trumpets blaring, I thought I recognized Uncle Ken's old bugle. A dark, good-looking youth blew vigorously upon it, quite out of tune with everyone else. It looked and sounded like Uncle Ken's bugle.

*

Summer came and went, and so did the mangoes. And then the monsoon arrived, and the pond behind the house overflowed, and there were frogs hopping about all over the veranda.

One morning Grandfather called me over to the back garden and led me down to the pond where he pointed to a couple of new arrivals—a pair of colourful storks who were wading about on their long legs and using their huge bills to snap up fish, frogs, or anything else they fancied. They paid no attention to us, and we were quite content to watch them going about their business.

Uncle Ken, of course, had to go and make a nuisance of himself. Armed with his Kodak 'Baby Brownie' camera (all the rage at the time), he waded into the pond (wearing Grandfather's boots) and proceeded to take pictures of the visiting birds.

Now, certain storks and cranes—especially those who move about in pairs—grow very attached to each other, and resent any overtures of friendship from clumsy humans.

Mr Stork, seeing Uncle Ken approaching through the lily-covered waters, assumed that my uncle's intentions were of an amorous nature. Uncle Ken in hat and cloak might well have been mistaken for a huge bird of prey—or a member of the ostrich family.

Mr Stock wasn't going to stand for any rivals, and leaving Mrs Stork to do the fishing, advanced upon Uncle Ken with surprising speed, lunged at him, and knocked the camera from his hands.

Leaving his camera to the tadpoles, Uncle Ken fled from the lily pond, hotly pursued by an irate stork, who even got in a couple of kung fu kicks before Uncle Ken reached the safety of the veranda.

Mourning the loss of his dignity and his camera, Uncle Ken sulked for a couple of days, and then announced that he was going to far-off Pondicherry, to stay with an aunt who had settled there.

Everyone heaved a sigh of relief, and Grandfather and I saw Uncle Ken off at the station, just to make sure he didn't change his mind and return home in time for dinner.

Later, we heard that Uncle Ken's holiday in Pondicherry went smoothly for a couple of days, there being no trees around his aunt's sea-front flat. On the beach he consumed innumberable ice creams and platters full of French fries, without being bothered by crows, parrots, monkeys or small boys.

And then, one morning, he decided to treat himself to breakfast at on open-air café near the beach, and ordered bacon and eggs, sausages, three toasts, cheese and marmalade.

He had barely taken a bite out of his buttered toast when, out of a blind blue sky, a seagull swooped down and carried off a sausage.

Uncle Ken was still in shock when another seagull shot past him, taking with it a rasher of bacon.

Seconds later a third gull descended and removed the remaining sausage, splattering toast and fried egg all over Uncle Ken's trousers.

He was left with half a toast and a small pot of marmalade.

When he got back to the flat and told his aunt what had happened, she felt sorry for him and gave him a glass of milk and a peanut butter sandwich.

Uncle Ken hated milk. And he detested peanut butter. But when hungry he would eat almost anything.

'Can't trust those seagulls,' said his aunt. 'They are all non-veg. Stick to spinach and lettuce, and they'll leave you alone.'

'Ugh,' said Uncle Ken in disgust. 'I'd rather be a seagull.'

A Crow for All Seasons

Early to bed and early to rise makes a crow healthy, wealthy and wise.

They say it's true for humans too. I'm not so sure about that. But for crows it's a must.

I'm always up at the crack of down, often the first crow to break the night's silence with a lusty caw. My friends and relatives, who roost in the same tree, grumble a bit and mutter to themselves, but they are soon cawing just as loudly. Long before the sun is up, we set off on the day's work.

We do not pause even for the morning wash. Later in the day, if it's hot and muggy, I might take a dip in some human's bathwater; but early in the morning we like to be up and about before everyone else. This is the time when trash cans and refuse dumps are overflowing with goodies, and we like to sift through them before the dustmen arrive in their disposal trucks.

Not that we are afraid of a famine in refuse. As human beings multiply, so does their rubbish.

Only yesterday I rescued an old typewriter ribbon from the dustbin, just before it was emptied. What a waste that would have been! I had no use for it myself, but I gave it to one of my cousins who got married recently, and she tells me it's just right for her nest, the one she's building on a telegraph pole. It helps her bind the twigs together, she says.

My own preference is for toothbrushes. They're just a hobby, really, like stamp-collecting with humans. I have a small but select collection which I keep in a hole in the garden wall. Don't ask me how many I've got—crows don't believe there's any point in counting beyond *two*—but I know there's more than one, that there's a whole lot of them in fact, because there isn't anyone living on this road who hasn't lost a toothbrush to me at some time or another.

We crows living in the jackfruit tree have this stretch of road to ourselves, but so that we don't quarrel or have misunderstandings, we've shared the houses out. I picked the bungalow with the orchard at the back. After all, I don't eat rubbish and throwaways all the time. Just occasionally I like a ripe guava or the soft flesh of a papaya. And sometimes I like the odd beetle as hors d'oeuvre. Those humans in the bungalow should be grateful to me for keeping down the population of fruit-eating beetles, and even for recycling their refuse; but no, humans are never grateful. No sooner do I settle in one of their guava trees than stones are whizzing past me. So I return to the dustbin on the back veranda steps. They don't mind my being there.

One of my cousins shares the bungalow with me, but he's a lazy fellow and I have to do most of the foraging. Sometimes I get him to lend me a claw; but most of the time he's preening his feathers and trying to look handsome for a pretty young thing who lives in the banyan tree at the next turning.

When he's in the mood, he can be invaluable, as he proved recently when I was having some difficulty getting at the dog's food on the veranda.

This dog, who is fussed over so much by the humans I've adopted, is a great big fellow, a mastiff who pretends to a pedigree going back to the time of Genghis Khan—he likes to pretend one of his ancestors was the great Khan's watchdog—but, as often happens in famous families, animal or human, there is a falling off in quality over a period of time, and this ugly fellow—Crazy, they call him—is a case in point. All brawn and no brain. Many a time I've removed a juicy bone from his plate or helped myself to pickings from under his nose.

But of late he's been growing canny and selfish. He doesn't like to share any more. And the other day I was almost in his jaws when he took a sudden lunge at me. Snap went his great teeth; but all he got was one of my tail feathers. He spat it out in disgust. Who wants crow's meat, anyway?

All the same, I thought, I'd better not be too careless. It's not for nothing that a crow's IQ is way above that of all other birds. And it's higher than a dog's, I bet.

*

I woke Cousin Slow from his midday siesta and said, 'Hey, Slow, we've got a problem. If you want any of that delicious tripe today, you've got to lend a claw—or a beak. That dog's getting snappier day by day.'

Slow opened one eye and said, 'Well, if you insist. But you know how I hate getting into a scuffle. It's bad for the gloss on my feathers.'

'I don't insist,' I said politely, 'but I'm not foraging for both of us today. It's every crow for himself.'

'Okay, okay, I'm coming,' said Slow, and with barely a flap he dropped down from the tree to the wall.

'What's the strategy?' I asked.

'Simple. We'll just give him the old one-two.'

We flew across to the veranda. Crazy had just started his meal. He was a fast, greedy eater who made horrible slurping sounds while he guzzled his food. We had to move fast if we wanted to get something before the meal was over.

I sidled up to Crazy and wished him good afternoon.

He kept on gobbling—but quicker now.

Slow came up from behind and gave him a quick peck near the tail—a sensitive spot—and, as Crazy swung round snarling, I moved in quickly and snatched up several tidbits.

Crazy went for me, and I flew freestyle for the garden wall. The dish was untended, so Slow helped himself to as many scraps as he could stuff in his mouth.

He joined me on the garden wall, and we sat there feasting, while Crazy barked himself hoarse below.

'Go catch a cat,' said Slow, who is given to slang. 'You're in the wrong league, big boy.'

The great sage Pratyasataka—ever heard of him? I guess not—once said, 'Nothing can improve a crow.'

Like most human sages, he wasn't very clear in his thinking, so there has been some misunderstanding about what he meant. Humans like to think that what he really meant was that crows were so bad as to be beyond improvement. But we crows know better. We interpret the saying as meaning that the crow is so perfect that no improvement is possible.

It's not that we aren't human—what I mean is, there are times when we fall from our high standards and do rather foolish things. Like at lunch time the other day.

Sometimes, when the table is laid in the bungalow, and before the family enters the dining room, I nip in through the open window and make a quick foray among the dishes. Sometimes I'm lucky enough to pick up a sausage or a slice of toast, or even a pat of butter, making off before someone enters and throws a bread knife at me. But on this occasion, just as I was reaching for the toast, a thin slouching fellow—Ken they call him—entered suddenly and shouted at me. I was so startled that I leapt across the table, seeking shelter. Something flew at me and in an effort to

dodge the missile I put my head through a circular object and then found it wouldn't come off.

It wasn't safe to hang around there, so I flew out of the window with this dashed ring still round my neck.

Serviette or napkin rings, that's what they are called. Quite unnecessary objects, but some humans—particularly the well-to-do sort—seem to like having them on their tables, holding bits of cloth in place. The cloth is used for wiping the mouth. Have you ever heard of such nonsense?

Anyway, there I was with a fat napkin ring around my neck, and as I perched on the wall trying to get it off, the entire human family gathered on their veranda to watch me.

There was the Bada* sahib and his wife, the memsahib; there was the scrawny Chhota sahib or Ken (worst of the lot); there was a mischievous boy (the Bada sahib's grandson) known as the Baba; and there was the cook (who usually flung orange peels at me) and the gardener (who once tried to decapitate me with a spade), and the dog Crazy who, like most dogs, tries unsuccessfully to be a human.

*Bada was a term used for a senior or elder member of the family.

Today, they weren't cursing and shaking their fists at me; they were just standing and laughing their heads off. What's so funny about a crow with its head stuck in a napkin ring?

Worse was to follow.

The noise had attracted the other crows in the area, and if there's one thing crows detest, it's a crow who doesn't look like a crow.

They swooped low and dived on me, hammering at the wretched napkin ring, until they had knocked me off the wall and into a flower bed. Then six or seven toughs landed on me with every intention of finishing me off.

'Hey, boys!' I cawed. 'This is me, Speedy! What are you trying to do—kill me?'

'That's right! You don't look like Speedy to us. What have you done with him, hey?'

And they set upon me with even greater vigour.

'You're just like a bunch of lousy humans!' I shouted. 'You're no better than them—this is just the way they carry on amongst themselves!'

That brought them to a halt. They stopped trying to peck me to pieces, and stood back, looking puzzled. The napkin ring had been shattered in the onslaught and had fallen to the ground.

'Why, it's Speedy!' said one of the gang.

'None other!'

'Good old Speedy—what are you doing here? And where's the guy we were hammering just now?'

There was no point in trying to explain things to them. Crows are like that. There're all good pals—until one of them tries to look different. Then he could be just another bird.

'He took off for Tibet,' I said. 'It was getting unhealthy for him around here.'

*

Summertime is here again. And although I'm a crow for all seasons, I must admit to a preference for the summer months.

Humans grow lazy and don't pursue me with so much vigour. Garbage cans overflow. Food goes bad and is constantly being thrown away. Overripe fruit gets tastier by the minute. If fellows like me weren't around to mop up all these unappreciated riches, how would humans manage?

There's one character in the bungalow, the Chhota sahib or Ken, who will never appreciate our services, it seems. He simply hates crows. The small boy may throw stones at us occasionally, but then, he's the sort who throws stones at almost anything. There's nothing personal about it. He just throws stones on principle.

The memsahib is probably the best of the lot. She often throws me scraps from the kitchen—onion skins, potato peels, crusts and leftovers—and even when I nip in and make off with something not meant for me (like a jam tart or a cheese pakora) she is quite sporting about it. Ken looks outraged, but the lady of the house says, 'Well, we've all got to make a living somehow, and that's how crows make theirs. It's high time you thought of earning a living.' Ken's her son—that's his occupation. He has never been known to work.

The Bada sahib has a sense of humour but it's often directed at me. He thinks I'm a comedian.

He discovered I'd been making off with the occasional egg from the egg basket on the veranda, and one day, without my knowledge, he made a substitution.

Right on top of the pile I found a smooth, round egg, and before anyone could shout 'Crow!', I'd made off with it. It was abnormally light. I put it down on the lawn and set about cracking it with my strong beak; but it would keep slipping away or bouncing off into the bushes. Finally, I got it between my feet and gave it a good hard whack. It burst open. To my utter astonishment there was nothing inside!

I looked up and saw the old man standing on the veranda, doubled up with laughter.

'What are you laughing at?' asked the memsahib, coming out to see what it was all about.

'It's that ridiculous crow!' guffawed the sahib, pointing at me. 'You know he's been stealing our eggs. Well, I placed a ping-pong ball on top of the pile, and he fell for it! He's been struggling with that ball for twenty minutes! That will teach him a lesson.'

It did. But I had my revenge later, when I pinched a brand new toothbrush from the sahib's bathroom.

*

This Ken has no sense of humour at all. He idles about the house and grounds all day, whistling or singing to himself.

'Even that crow sings better than Uncle,' said the boy.

A truthful boy; but all he got for his honesty was a whack on the head from his uncle.

Anyway, as a gesture of appreciation, I perched on the garden wall and gave the family a rendering of my favourite crow song, which is my own composition. Here it is, translated for your benefit:

Oh, for the life of a crow!
A bird who's in the know,
Although we are cursed,
We are never dispersed—
We're always on the go

I know I'm a bit of a rogue
(And my voice wouldn't pass for a brogue).
But there's no one as sleek
Or as neat with his beak—
So they're putting my picture in *Vogue*!

Oh, for the life of a crow!
I reap what I never sow,
They call me a thief—
Pray I'll soon come to grief—
But there's no getting rid of a crow!

I gave it everything I had, and the humans—all of them on the lawn to enjoy the evening breeze, listened to me in silence, struck with wonder at my performance.

When I had finished, I bowed and preened myself, waiting for the applause.

They stared at each other for a few seconds. Then Ken stooped, picked up a bottle opener, and flung it at me.

Well, I ask you!

What can one say about humans? I do my best to defend them from all kinds of criticism, and this is what I get for my pains.

Anyway, I picked up the bottle opener and added it to my collection of odds and ends.

It was getting dark, and soon everyone was stumbling around, looking for another bottle opener. Ken's popularity was even lower than mine.

*

One day Ken came home carrying a heavy shotgun. He pointed it at me a few times and I dived for cover. But he didn't fire. Probably, I was out of range.

'He's only threatening you,' said Slow, from the safety of the jamun tree, where he sat in the shadows. 'He probably doesn't know how to fire the thing.'

But I wasn't taking any chances. I'd seen a sly look on Ken's face, and I decided that he was trying to make me careless. So I stayed well out of range.

Then one evening I received a visit from my cousin brother, Charm. He'd come to me for a loan. He wanted some new bottle caps for his collection and brought me a mouldy old toothbrush in exchange.

Charm landed on the garden wall, toothbrush in his beak, and was waiting for me to join him there, when there was a flash and a tremendous bang. Charm was sent several feet into the air, and landed limp and dead in a flower bed.

'I've got him, I've got him!' shouted Ken. 'I've shot that blasted crow!'

Throwing away the gun, Ken ran out into the garden, overcome with joy. He picked up my fallen relative, and began running around the bungalow with his trophy.

The rest of the family had collected on the veranda.

'Drop that thing at once!' called the memsahib.

'Uncle is doing a war dance,' observed the boy.

'It's unlucky to shoot a crow,' said the Bada sahib.

I thought it was time to take a hand in the proceedings and let everyone know that the *right* crow—the one and only Speedy—was alive and kicking. So I swooped down the jackfruit tree, dived through Ken's window and emerged with one of his socks.

Triumphantly flaunting his dead crow, Ken came dancing up the garden path, then stopped dead when he saw me perched on the window sill, a sock in my beak. His jaw fell, his eyes bulged; he looked like the owl in the banyan tree.

'You shot the wrong crow!' shouted the sahib, and everyone roared with laughter.

Before Ken could recover from the shock, I took off in leisurely fashion and joined Slow on the wall.

Ken came rushing out with the gun, but by now it was too dark to see anything, and I heard the memsahib telling the sahib, 'You'd better take that gun away before he does himself a mischief.' So the sahib took Ken indoors and gave him a brandy.

I composed a new song for Ken's benefit and sang it to him outside his window early next morning:

I understand you want a crow
To poison, shoot or smother;
My fond salaams, but by your leave
I'll substitute another:

Allow me then, to introduce
My most respected brother.

Although I was quite understanding about the whole tragic mix-up—I was, after all, the family's very own house-crow—my fellow crows were outraged at what happened to Charm, and swore vengeance on Ken.

'*Corvus splendens!*' they shouted with great spirit, forgetting that this title had been bestowed on us by a human.

In times of war, we forget how much we owe to our enemies.

Ken had only to step into the garden, and several crows would sweep down on him, screeching and swearing and aiming lusty blows at his head and hands. He took to coming out wearing a sola-topee, and even then they knocked it off and drove him indoors. Once he tried lighting a cigarette on the veranda steps, when Slow swooped low across the porch and snatched it from his lips.

Every now and then the memsahib would come out and shoo us off; and because she wasn't an enemy, we obliged by retreating to the garden wall. After all, Slow and I depended on her for much of our board if not for our lodging. But Ken had only to show his face outside the house, and all the crows in the area would be after him like avenging furies.

'It doesn't look as though they are going to forgive you,' said the memsahib.

'Elephants never forget, and crows never forgive,' said the sahib.

'Would you like to borrow my catapult, Uncle?' asked the boy. 'Just for self-protection, you know.'

'Shut up,' said Ken and went to bed.

One day he sneaked out of the back door and dashed across to the garage. A little later, the family's old car, seldom used, came out of the garage with Ken at the wheel. He'd decided that if he couldn't take a walk in safety, he'd go for a drive. All the windows were up.

No sooner had the car turned into the driveway than about a dozen crows dived down on it, crowding the bonnet and flipping in front of the windscreen. Ken couldn't see a thing. He swung the steering wheel left, right and centre, and the car went off the driveway, ripped through a hedge, crushed a bed of sweet peas and came to a stop against the trunk of a mango tree.

Ken just sat there, afraid to open the door. The family had to come out of the house and rescue him.

'Are you all right?' asked the Bada sahib.

'I've bruised my knees,' said Ken.

'Never mind your knees,' said the memsahib, gazing around at the ruin of her garden. 'What about my sweet peas?'

'I think your uncle is going to have a nervous breakdown,' I heard the Bada sahib saying.

'What's that?' asked the boy. 'Is it the same as a car having a breakdown?'

'Well—not exactly . . . But you could call it a mind breaking up.'

Ken had been refusing to leave his room or take his meals. The family was worried about him. I was worried, too. Believe it or not, we crows are among the very few who sincerely desire the preservation of the human species.

'He needs a change,' said the memsahib.

'A rest cure,' said the Bada sahib sarcastically. 'A rest from doing nothing.'

'Send him to Switzerland,' suggested the boy.

'We can't afford that. But we can take him up to a hill station.'

The nearest hill station was some thirty miles as the human drives (only five as the crow flies). Many people went up during the summer months. It wasn't fancied much by crows.

For one thing, it was a tidy sort of place, and people lived in houses that were set fairly far apart. Opportunities for scavenging were limited. Also, it was rather cold and the trees were inconvenient and uncomfortable. A friend of mine who had spent a night in a pine tree said he hadn't been able to sleep because of prickly pine needles and the wind howling through the branches.

'Let's all go up for a holiday,' said the memsahib. 'We can spend a week in a boarding house. All of us need a change.'

A few days later the house was locked up, and the family piled into the old car and drove off to the hills.

I had the grounds to myself.

The dog had gone too, and the gardener spent all day dozing in his hammock. There was no one around to trouble me.

'We've got the whole place to ourselves,' I told Slow.

'Yes, but what good is that? With everyone

gone, there are no throwaways, give-aways and takeaways!'

'We'll have to try the house next door.'

'And be driven off by the other crows? That's not our territory, you know. We can go across to help them, or to ask for their help, but we're not supposed to take their pickings. It just isn't cricket, old boy.'

We could have tried the bazaar or the railway station, where there is always a lot of rubbish to be found, but there is also a lot of competition in those places. The station crows are gangsters. The bazaar crows are bullies. Slow and I had grown soft. We'd have been no match for the bad boys.

'I've just realized how much we depend on humans,' I said.

'We could go back to living in the jungle,' said Slow.

'No, that would be too much like hard work. We'd be living on wild fruit most of the time. Besides, the jungle crows won't have anything to do with us now. Ever since we took up with humans, we became the outcastes of the bird world.'

'That means we're almost human.'

'You might say we have all their vices and none of their virtues.'

'Just a different set of values, old boy.'

'Like eating hens' eggs instead of crows' eggs. That's something in their favour. And while you're hanging around here waiting for the mangoes to fall, I'm off to locate our humans.'

Slow's beak fell open. He looked like—well, a hungry crow.

'Don't tell me you're going to follow them up to the hill station? You don't even know where they are staying.'

'I'll soon find out,' I said, and took off for the hills.

You'd be surprised at how simple it is to be a good detective, if only you put your mind to it. Of course, if Ellery Queen had been able to fly, he wouldn't have required fifteen chapters and his father's assistance to crack a case.

Swooping low over the hill station, it wasn't long before I spotted my humans' old car. It was parked outside a boarding house called the Climber's Rest. I hadn't seen anyone climbing, but, dozing in an armchair in the garden, was my favourite human.

I perched on top of a colourful umbrella and waited for Ken to wake up. I decided it would be rather inconsiderate of me to disturb his sleep, so I waited patiently on the brolly, looking at him with one eye and keeping one eye on the house. He stirred uneasily, as though he'd suddenly had a bad dream; then he opened his eyes. I must have been the first thing he saw.

'Good morning,' I cawed, in a friendly tone— always ready to forgive and forget, that's Speedy!

He leapt out of the armchair and ran into the house, hollering at the top of his voice.

I supposed he hadn't been able to contain his delight at seeing me again. Humans can be funny that way. They'll hate you one day and love you the next.

Well, Ken ran all over the boarding house, screaming, 'It's that crow, it's that crow! He's following me everywhere!'

Various people, including the family, ran outside to see what the commotion was about, and I thought it would be better to make myself scarce. So I flew to the top of a spruce tree and stayed very still and quiet.

'Crow! What crow?' said the Bada sahib.

'Our crow!' cried Ken. 'The one that persecutes me. I was dreaming of it just now, and when I opened my eyes, there it was, on the garden umbrella!'

'There's nothing there now,' said the memsahib. 'You probably hadn't woken up completely.'

'He is having illusions again,' said the boy.

'Delusions,' corrected the Bada sahib.

'Now look here,' said the memsahib. 'You'll have to pull yourself together. You'll take leave of your senses if you don't.'

'I tell you, it's here!' sobbed Ken. 'It's following me everywhere.'

'It's grown fond of Uncle,' said the boy. 'And it seems Uncle can't live without crows.'

Ken looked up with a wild glint in his eye.

'That's it!' he cried. 'I can't live without them. That's the answer to my problem. I don't hate crows—I love them!'

Everyone just stood around, goggling at Ken.

'I'm feeling fine now,' he carried on. 'What a difference it makes if you can just do the opposite to what you've been doing before!' And flapping his arms, and trying to caw like a crow, he went prancing about the garden.

'Now he thinks he's a crow,' said the boy. 'Is he still having delusions?'

'That's right,' said the memsahib. 'Delusions of grandeur.'

After that, the family decided that there was no point in staying on in the hill station any longer.

Ken had completed his rest cure. And even if he was the only one who believed himself cured, that was all right, because after all he was the one who mattered . . . If you're feeling fine, can there be anything wrong with you?

No sooner was everyone back in the bungalow than Ken took to hopping barefoot on the grass early every morning, all the time scattering food about for the crows. Bread, chapatties, cooked rice, curried eggplants, the memsahib's home-made toffee—you name it, we got it!

Slow and I were the first to help ourselves to these dawn offerings, and soon the other crows had joined us on the lawn. We didn't mind. Ken brought enough for everyone.

'We ought to honour him in some way,' said Slow.

'Yes, why not?' said I. 'There was someone else, hundreds of years ago, who fed the birds. They followed him wherever he went.'

'That's right. They made him a saint, Saint Francis. But as far as I know, he didn't feed any crows. At least, you don't see any crows in the pictures—just sparrows and robins and wagtails.'

'Small fry. *Our* human is dedicated exclusively to crows. Do you realize that, Slow?'

'Sure. We ought to make him the patron saint of crows. What do you say, fellows?'

'Caw, caw, caw!' All the crows were in agreement.

'St. Corvus!' said Slow, as Ken emerged from the house, laden with good things to eat.

'Corvus, corvus, corvus!' we cried.

And what a pretty picture he made—a crow eating from his hand, another perched on his shoulder, and about a dozen of us on the grass, forming a respectful ring around him.

From persecutor to protector; from beastliness to saintliness. And sometimes it can be the other way round: you never know with humans!

Uncle Ken Goes
Birdwatching

'Where have all the birds gone?' asked Uncle Ken, on a sunny December morning.

At first I thought he was on the subject of a local beauty contest, and I answered: 'To Hollywood, of course, to see Gregory *Peck*.'

Not being a movie-goer, Uncle Ken missed out on the pun, but he corrected himself and said, 'No, I mean the sparrows. Where have all the sparrows gone?'

This had me baffled. I knew nothing about the sparrows going anywhere, but then, I had never paid much attention to their comings and goings. One is inclined to take sparrows for granted.

'Why do you ask?' I asked.

'Because I've heard they're disappearing. How can we have a world without sparrows?'

'You're thinking of the mountain quail,' I said. 'Sparrows aren't going extinct.'

'Well, I haven't seen any for a long time. And they used to be all over the place. On the veranda steps, at the kitchen window, in the backyard . . . once, they even made a nest in one of my old hats.'

Uncle Ken had a collection of hats—felt hats, bowler hats, straw hats, floppy hats, pith helmets—and they would lie about in different places and occasionally be forgotten. Three baby mice were discovered in an old bowler hat, a squirrel stored nuts in an old sun-helmet; and a small bat made its home in a felt hat that had been hanging too long on the veranda wall.

Uncle Ken seldom went out without a hat of sorts. He did not have much hair or his head and he was afraid of getting sunstroke.

On this particular morning he was wearing a peaked hunting-cap, rather like the one used by Sherlock Holmes. It seemed to go with his new-found interest in birds.

'Sparrows,' he repeated. 'What would life be like without sparrows?'

I gave it some thought and said, 'Not very different, I suppose. There would still be other birds.'

'Ah, but would there? If the sparrows go, will the rest be far behind?'

Uncle Ken had a point.

'I would hate to see all the chickens fly away,' I said.

'Why so?'

'Because I like chicken curry.'

'You're just a hedonist, Ruskin. Have you no soul? Imagine a world without beautiful peacocks, swans, nightingales, parakeets, geese, ducks . . .'

'Granny makes a good duck curry,' I interjected.

'Kingfishers, cranes, seagulls,' continued Uncle Ken.

'We don't get seagulls here,' I said. 'Go back to Pondicherry.'

'All right, then, partridges, cormorants, turkeys . . .'

'Roast turkey for Christmas. We'll ask Grandfather to get one. And what about crows, Uncle Ken? You've forgotten the crows. You are very popular with them.'

'Plenty of crows about. They are in no danger of extinction. But we have to do something about the sparrows. Where have all the sparrows gone?'

'They've gone next door,' I told him. 'Hadn't you noticed?' And I led him across the garden to the boundary wall, which gave us a clear view of our neighbour's side veranda. There we saw Colonel Mehandru (retired) scattering grain on the veranda steps, while hundreds of sparrows crowded round him, pecking away at the Colonel's largesse.

'A few bread crumbs won't do,' I told Uncle Ken. 'Buckets of birdseed is what they want. Get some bajra and see the difference!'

So off went Uncle Ken, determined to outdo the Colonel's popularity with the sparrow fraternity. He returned from the bazaar with a sackful of bajra, and began scattering the seeds all over the compound. The squirrels were delighted and so were the hens, but it took some time for the sparrows to reconvert to their former allegiance. Some of them did come over, but as there was plenty of birdseed to be had on the Colonel's side of the wall, there was no great rush to return to our side.

'Is the Colonel's bajra superior to ours?' asked Uncle Ken.

'I'll find out,' I said, and in the afternoon, while the Colonel was taking his siesta, I climbed over the wall, walked up to the veranda steps, and filled my pockets with some of the grain that had been strewn around the place. When I got back to our place, we examined the grain, but were none the wiser; so we consulted Granny.

'It's not bajra,' said Granny. 'That's kangni—it's a smaller seed, easier for small birds to pick up and ingest.'

So off went Uncle Ken again but he had a hard time finding kangni; the grain merchants did not bother to stock it, as it was strictly for the birds! Apparently Colonel Mehandru had a secret supply.

Not to be discouraged, Uncle Ken continued to scatter bajra in all directions, and soon had a faithful following of pigeons. And this was to lead to his taking up birdwatching in a more ambitious manner.

*

'These pigeons are all very well,' said Uncle Ken one day. 'But I want to see a green pigeon.'

'Well, I can paint one of these green, if you like,' I offered. 'I'm sure the pigeon won't mind.'

'Don't be an idiot,' said Uncle Ken. 'I want to see the real thing.'

'Are green pigeons very rare, then?'

'Not really. But they are not city birds, like these.

They live in trees and don't come down to the ground.'

'What do they live on then?'

'Wild fruit, of course. Berries etc.'

He'd been reading up Salim Ali's and Whistler's bird books and was showing off his new-found knowledge.

Dhuki, Granny's old gardener, had mentioned that green pigeons could sometimes be seen in a big banyan tree that grew near Rajpur, at the base of the foothills. It was about five miles from our house.

'Be up early tomorrow,' said Uncle Ken. 'We're going birdwatching. Green pigeons!'

'I was going to play cricket tomorrow morning.'

'Cricket! Such a waste of time. The forest beckons, nature is calling, the wide open spaces are yours to explore—and all you can think of is hitting a ball around the maidaan.'

'Actually, I'm a bowler, not a batsman.'

'What could be worse. All that energy spent in flinging a ball at someone who's going to hit it for six anyway!'

It was no use arguing with Uncle Ken—not when he was in the grip of one of his sudden enthusiasms.

This was the year of the Bird, as far as he was concerned, and nothing else mattered.

He produced an old pair of binoculars which he had found in the storeroom.

'What are those for?' I asked

'Watching birds, what else?'

I took the binoculars from him and looked them over. 'There's a date stamped here. 1914. Grandfather must have used them in World War I.'

'Well, that shouldn't stop us from using them now.'

I raised them to my eyes and looked out across the garden to where Dhuki was weeding the flower beds. He was just a blur.

'Out of focus,' I said. 'You'll see better without them.'

'We'll take them along anyway. To look more professional.'

*

Uncle Ken was normally a late riser, but such was his enthusiasm for his new vocation that he was up at the crack of dawn, whistling cheerfully as he turned me out of my bed.

'Up with the lark!' he called.'Come, listen to the morning thrush!'

'We don't get larks in Dehra,' I said. 'And it's the whistling thrush, not the morning thrush.'

'Well, it's a beautiful morning, and we're going to have a great day. What a lark!'

It didn't take me long to get dressed, but Uncle Ken was ready before me, looking like a scoutmaster in his shorts (displaying his bandy-legs), bush-shirt and felt hat with one side turned up quite rakishly.

The bicycles were brought out, and off we went.

'We'll be back in time for breakfast,' said Uncle Ken. He never missed breakfast.

It took us half an hour to reach Rajpur, and the sun was just coming up, sending its shafts of gold through the branches of the great banyan tree that stood outside the village. The tree was alive with birds, and we were free to feast our eyes an parakeets, rosy pastors, bulbuls and other arboreal creatures, but Uncle Ken was determined to locate a green pigeon, and was convinced that he had seen a couple creeping along upside down in the upper branches of the great tree. Handing me the binoculars he proceeded to climb the tree, not too difficult a task, as the banyan has many supporting limbs. I trained the binoculars on the upper branches of the tree, and called out: 'They are not pigeons, Uncle, they're flying foxes!'

Flying foxes are fruit-eating bats, and whole colonies can sometimes be found in one tree, resting upside down, apparently fast asleep.

But Uncle Ken wasn't listening. He had eyes only for green pigeons, and he ascended the tree until he was in the midst of the roosting flying foxes. They did not take kindly to his sudden appearance. Squeals of anger were followed by a great whirring sound, and scores of bats rose into the air, circling the top of the tree. Two or three swooped down on Uncle Ken, who made a rapid descent, fending off the bats with one arm while clinging to branches with the other. He came down in a most undignified fashion, losing his hat and tearing his shorts. Two of the little creatures were still attached to his collar, and Uncle Ken shouted, 'Knock them off, knock them off!'

I removed them with the help of his hat, and Uncle Ken sat down on the grass and querulously asked, 'Am I bleeding? I think I've been bitten.'

'I don't think so,' I said. 'Just a couple of scratches on your neck.'

'Vampire bats!' moaned Uncle Ken. 'Very infectious. I could go mad!'

I forbore from saying he was already quite mad, but made things even worse by remarking, 'You could become a vampire, Uncle Ken. Like Dracula, you know.'

He went quite pale, gulped, and said, 'Do you really think so, Ruskin?'

'Then you can go around biting people and sucking their blood. What fun!'

'Let's go home,' said Uncle Ken. 'We'll look for the green pigeons another day.'

We returned in time for breakfast, but Uncle Ken barely touched his. He looked very despondent for the rest of the day, and I could see he was very worried about those scratches or bites. I was curious to see if he would develop any of the traits of a vampire, and followed him about wherever he went. On one occasion, I saw him looking speculatively at Aunt Mabel's neck, and I thought he was going to sink his teeth into her flesh. Aunt Mabel a vampire! Now that would have been something.

But Uncle Ken desisted from biting her, although I could see that he really wanted to. After a few days he recovered his high spirits and began enjoying his breakfast.

Then one day he grabbed me by the arm and said, 'The red jungle fowl, do you know that it's almost extinct? I must see one before it's too late!'

Uncle Ken's Rumble in the Jungle

Uncle Ken drove Grandfather's old Fiat along the forest road at an incredible 30 mph, scattering pheasants, partridges and jungle fowl as he clattered along. He had come in search of the disappearing red jungle fowl, and I could see why the bird had disappeared. Too many noisy human beings had invaded its habitat.

By the time we reached the forest rest house, one of the car doors had fallen off its hinges, and a large lantana bush had got entwined in the bumper.

'Never mind,' said Uncle Ken. 'It's all part of the adventure!'

The rest house had been reserved for Uncle Ken, thanks to Grandfather's good relations with the forest department. But I was the only other person in the car. No one else would trust himself or herself to

Uncle Ken's driving. He treated a car as though it were a low-flying aircraft having some difficulty in getting off the runway.

As we arrived at the rest house, a number of hens made a dash for safety.

'Look, jungle fowl!' exclaimed Uncle Ken.

'Domestic fowl,' I said. 'They must belong to the forest guards.'

I was right, of course. One of the hens was destined to be served up as chicken curry later that day. The jungle birds avoided the neighourhood of the rest house, just in case they were mistaken for poultry and went into the cooking pot.

Uncle Ken was all for starting his search right away, and after a brief interval during which we were served with tea and pakoras (prepared by the forest guard, who it turned out was also a good cook) we set off on foot into the jungle in search of the elusive red jungle fowl.

'No tigers around here, are there?' asked Uncle Ken, just to be on the safe side.

'No tigers on this range,' said the guard. 'Just elephants.'

Uncle Ken wasn't afraid of elephants. He'd been for numerous elephant rides at the Lucknow zoo. He'd also seen Sabu in *Elephant Boy*.

A small wooden bridge took us across a little river, and then we were in thick jungle, following the forest guard who led us along a path that was frequently blocked by broken tree branches and pieces of bamboo.

'Why all these broken branches?' asked Uncle Ken.

'The elephants, sir,' replied our guard. 'They passed through last night. They like certain leaves, as well as young bamboo shoots.'

We saw a number of spotted deer and several pheasants, but no red jungle fowl. That evening we sat out on the veranda of the rest house. All was silent, except for the distant trumpeting of elephants. Then, from the stream, came the chanting of hundreds of frogs.

There were tenors and baritones, sopranos and contraltos, and occasionally a bass deep enough to have pleased the great Chaliapin. They sang duets and quartets from *La Boheme* and other Italian operas, drowning out all other jungle sounds except for the occasional cry of a jackal doing his best to join in.

'We might as well sing,' said Uncle Ken, and began singing the 'Indian love call' in his best Nelson Eddy manner.

The frogs fell silent, obviously awestruck; but instead of receiving an answering love call, Uncle Ken was answered by even more strident jackal calls—not one, but several—with the result that all self-respecting denizens of the forest fled from the vicinity, and we saw no wildlife that night apart from a frightened rabbit that sped across the clearing and vanished into the darkness.

Early next morning we renewed our efforts to track down the red jungle fowl, but it remained elusive. Returning to the rest house dusty and weary, Uncle Ken exclaimed: 'There it is—a red jungle fowl!'

But it turned out to be the caretaker's cock-bird, a handsome fellow all red and gold, but not the jungle variety.

Disappointed, Uncle Ken decided to return to civilization. Another night in the rest house did not appeal to him. He had run out of songs to sing.

In any case, the weather had changed overnight and a light drizzle was falling as we started out. This had turned to a steady downpour by the time we reached the bridge across the Suswa river. And standing in the middle of the bridge was an elephant.

He was a lone tusker and didn't look too friendly.

Uncle Ken blew his horn, and that was a mistake.

It was a strident, penetrating horn, highly effective on city roads but out of place in the forest. The elephant took it as a challenge, and returned the blast of the horn with a shrill trumpeting of its own. It took a few steps forward. Uncle Ken put the car into reverse.

'Is there another way out of here?' he asked.

'There's a side road,' I said recalling an earlier trip with Grandfather. 'It will take us to the Kansrao railway station.'

'What ho!' cried Uncle Ken. 'To the station we go!'

And he turned the car and drove back until we came to the turning.

The narrow road was now a rushing torrent of rain water and all Uncle Ken's driving skills were put to the test. He had on one occasion driven through a brick wall, so he knew all about obstacles; but they were normally stationary ones.

'More elephants,' I said, as two large pachyderms loomed out of the rain-drenched forest.

'Elephants to the right of us, elephants to the left of us!' chanted Uncle Ken, misquoting Tennysons's 'Charge of the Light Brigade'. 'Into the valley of death rode the six hundred!'

'There are now three of them,' I observed.

'Not my lucky number,' said Uncle Ken and pressed hard on the accelerator. We lurched forward, almost running over a terrified barking deer.

'Is four your lucky number, Uncle Ken?'

'Why do you ask?'

'Well, there are now four of them behind us. And they are catching up quite fast!'

'I see the station ahead,' cried Uncle Ken, as we drove into a clearing where a tiny railway station stood like a beacon of safety in the wilderness.

The car came to a grinding halt. We abandoned it and ran for the building.

The stationmaster saw our predicament and beckoned to us to enter the station building, which was little more than a two-room shed and platform. He look us inside his tiny control room and shut the steel gate behind us.

'The elephants won't bother you here,' he said. 'But say goodbye to your car.'

We looked out of the window and were horrified to see Grandfather's Fiat overturned by one of the elephants, while another proceeded to trample it underfoot. The other elephants joined in the mayhem and soon the car was a flattened piece of junk.

'I'm Stationmaster Abdul Rauf,' the friendly stationmaster introduced himself. 'I know a good scrap dealer in Doiwala. I'll give you his address.'

'But how do we get out of here?' asked Uncle Ken.

'Well, it's only an hour's walk to Doiwala,' said our benefactor. 'But I wouldn't advise walking, not with those elephants around. Stay and have a cup of tea. The Dehra Express will pass through shortly. It stops for a few minutes. And it's only half an hour to Dehra from here.'

He punched out a couple of rail tickets. 'Here you are, my friends. Just two rupees each. The cheapest rail journey in India. And those tickets carry an insurance value of two lakh rupees each, should an accident befall you between here and Dehradun.'

Uncle Ken's eyes lit up. 'You mean, if one of us falls out of the train?' he asked.

'Out of the moving train,' clarified the stationmaster. 'There will be an enquiry, of course. Some people try to fake an accident.'

But Uncle Ken decided against falling out of the train and making a fortune. He'd had enough excitement for the day. We got home safely enough, taking a pony-cart from the Dehra station to our house.

'Where's my car?' asked Grandfather, as we staggered up the veranda steps.

'It had a small accident,' said Uncle Ken. 'We left it outside the Kansrao railway station. I'll collect it later.'

'I'm starving,' I said. 'Haven't eaten since morning.'

'Well, come and have your dinner,' said Granny. 'I've made something special for you. One of your Grandfather's hunting friends sent us a jungle fowl. I've made a nice roast. Try it with apple sauce.'

Uncle Ken did not ask if the jungle fowl was red, grey or technicoloured. He was first to the dining table.

Granny had anticipated this, and served me with a chicken leg, giving the other leg to Grandfather.

'I rather fancy the breast myself,' she said, and this left Uncle Ken with a long and scrawny neck—which was rather like his own neck, and more than he deserved.

At Sea with Uncle Ken

With Uncle Ken, you had always to expect the unexpected. Even in the most normal circumstances, something unusual would happen to him and to those around him. He was a catalyst for confusion.

My mother should have known better than to ask him to accompany me to England, the year after I'd finished school. She felt that a boy of sixteen was a little too young to make the voyage on his own. I might get lost or lose my money or fall overboard or catch some dreadful disease. She should have realized that Uncle Ken, her brother (well spoilt by all his sisters), was more likely to do all these things.

Anyway, he was put in charge of me and instructed to deliver me safely to an aunt in England, after which he could either stay there or return to India, whichever he preferred. Granny had paid for his ticket, so in effect he was getting a free holiday, which included a voyage on a posh P & O liner.

*

Our train journey to Bombay* passed off without incident, although Uncle Ken did manage to misplace his spectacles, getting down at the station wearing someone else's. This left him a little short-sighted, which might have accounted for his mistaking the stationmaster for a porter and instructing him to look after our luggage.

We had two days in Bombay before boarding the *S.S. Strathnaver* and Uncle Ken vowed that we would enjoy ourselves. However, he was a little constrained by his budget and took me to a rather seedy hotel on Lamington Road, where we had to share a toilet with over twenty other people.

'Never mind,' he said. 'We won't spend much time in this dump.' So he took me to Marine Drive and the Gateway of India, and then to an Irani restaurant in Colaba, where we enjoyed a super dinner of curried prawns and scented rice. I don't know if it was the curry, the prawns, or the scent,

*Now Mumbai.

but Uncle Ken was up all night, running back and forth to that toilet, so that no one else had a chance to use it. Several dispirited travellers simply opened the windows and ejected into space, cursing Uncle Ken all the while.

He had recovered by morning and proposed a trip to the Elephanta Caves. After a breakfast of fish pickle, a Malabari chilli chutney and sweet Gujarati puris, we got into a launch, accompanied by several other tourists, and set off on our short cruise. The sea was rather choppy, and we hadn't gone far before Uncle Ken decided to share his breakfast with the fishes of the sea. He was as green as seaweed by the time we went ashore. Uncle Ken collapsed on the sand and refused to move, so we didn't see much of the caves. I brought him some coconut water and he revived a bit and suggested we go on a fast until it was time to board our ship.

We were safely on board the following morning and the ship sailed majestically out from Ballard Pier, Bombay, and India receded into the distance, quite possibly forever as I wasn't sure that I would ever return. The sea fascinated me and I remained on deck all day, gazing at small craft, passing steamers, sea-birds, the distant shoreline, the surge of the waves, and of course my fellow passengers. I could well understand the fascination it held for writers such as Conrad, Stevenson, Maugham and others.

Uncle Ken, however, remained confined to his cabin. The rolling of the ship made him feel extremely ill. If he had been looking green in Bombay, he was looking yellow at sea. I took my meals in the dining saloon, where I struck up an acquaintance with a well-known palmist and fortune teller who was on his way to London to make his fortune. He looked at my hand and told me I'd never be rich, but that I'd help other people get rich.

When Uncle Ken felt better (on the third day of the voyage) he struggled up on the deck, took large lungfuls of sea air, and subsided into a deckchair. He dozed the day away, but was suddenly wide awake when an attractive blonde strode past us on her way to the lounge. After some time we heard the tinkling of a piano. Intrigued, Uncle Ken rose and staggered into the lounge. The girl was at the piano playing something classical, which wasn't something that Uncle Ken normally enjoyed. But he was smitten by the girl's good looks and stood enraptured. His eyes gleaming brightly, his jaw sagging with his nose pressed against the glass of the lounge door, he reminded me of a goldfish who has fallen in love with an angel fish that has just been introduced into the tank.

'What is she playing?' he whispered, aware that I had grown up on my late father's classical record collection.

'Rachmaninoff,' I made a guess. 'Or maybe Rimsky-Korsakov!'

'Something easier to pronounce,' he begged.

'Chopin,' I said.

'And what's his most famous composition?'

'Polonaise in A Flat. Or maybe it's A Major.'

He pushed open the lounge door, walked in, and when the girl had finished playing, applauded loudly. She acknowledged his applause with a smile, and then went on to play something else. When she had finished he clapped again and said, 'Wonderful! Chopin never sounded better!'

'Actually, it's Tchaikovsky,' said the girl. But she didn't seem to mind.

Uncle Ken would turn up at all her practice sessions, and very soon they were strolling the decks together. She was Australian, on her way to London to pursue a musical career as a concert pianist. I don't know what she saw in Uncle Ken, but he was good at giving people the impression that he knew all the right people. And he was quite good looking in an effete sort of way.

Left to my own devices, I followed my fortune-telling friend around and watched him study the palms of our fellow passengers. He foretold romance, travel, success, happiness, health, wealth and longevity, but never predicted anything that might upset anyone. As he did not charge anything (he was, after all, on holiday) he proved to be a popular passenger throughout the voyage. Later he was to become quite famous as a palmist and mind-reader, an Indian 'Cheiro', much in demand in the capitals of Europe.

The voyage lasted eighteen days, with stops for passengers and cargo at Aden, Port Said and Marseilles, in that order. It was at Port Said that Uncle Ken and his friend went ashore, to look at the sights and do some shopping.

'You stay on the ship,' Uncle Ken told me. 'Port Said isn't safe for young boys.'

He wanted the girl all to himself, of course. He couldn't have shown off with me around. His 'man of the world' manner would not have been very convincing in my presence.

The ship was due to sail again that evening and passengers had to be back on board an hour before departure. The hours passed easily enough for me, as the little library kept me engrossed. If there are books around, I am never bored. Towards evening I went up on deck and saw Uncle Ken's friend coming up the gangway, but of Uncle Ken there was no sign.

'Where's Uncle?' I asked her.

'Hasn't he returned? We got separated in a busy marketplace and I thought he'd get here before me.'

We stood at the railings and looked up and down the pier, expecting to see Uncle Ken among the other returning passengers. But he did not turn up.

'I suppose he's looking for you,' I said. 'He'll miss the boat if he doesn't hurry.'

The ship's hooter sounded. 'All aboard,' called the captain on his megaphone. The big ship moved slowly out of the harbour. We were on our way! In the distance I saw a figure that looked like Uncle Ken running along the pier, frantically waving his arms. But there was no turning back.

A few days later my aunt met me at Tilbury Dock.

'Where's your Uncle Ken?' she asked.

'He stayed behind at Port Said. He went ashore and didn't get back in time.'

'Just like Ken. And I don't suppose he has much money with him. Well, if he gets in touch we'll send him a postal order.'

But Uncle Ken failed to get in touch. He was a topic of discussion for several days, while I settled down in my aunt's house and looked for a job. At seventeen I was working in an office, earning a modest salary and contributing towards my aunt's housekeeping expenses. There was no time to worry about Uncle Ken's whereabouts.

My readers know that I longed to return to India, but it was nearly four years before that became possible. Finally I did come home and, as the train drew into Dehra's little station, I looked out of the window and saw a familiar figure on the platform. It was Uncle Ken!

He made no reference to his disappearance at Port Said, and greeted me as though we had last seen each other the previous day.

'I've hired a cycle for you,' he said. 'Feel like a ride?'

'Let me get home first, Uncle Ken. I've got all this luggage.'

The luggage was piled into a tonga, I sat on top

of everything, and we went clip-clop down an avenue of familiar litchi trees. Uncle Ken rode behind the tonga, whistling cheerfully.

'When did you get back to Dehra?' I asked.

'Oh, a couple of years ago. Sorry I missed the boat. Was the girl upset?'

'She said she'd never forgive you.'

'Oh well, I expect she's better off without me. Fine piano player. Chopin and all that stuff.'

'Did Granny send you the money to come home?'

'No Ruskin, I had to take a job working as a waiter in a Greek restaurant. Then I took tourists to look at the pyramids. I'm an expert on pyramids now. Great place, Egypt. But I had to leave when they found I had no papers or permit. They put me on a boat to Aden. Stayed in Aden for six months teaching English to the son of a Sheikh. Sheikh's son went to England, I came back to India.'

'And what are you doing now, Uncle Ken?'

'Thinking of starting a poultry farm; lots of space behind the house. Maybe you can help me with it.'

'I couldn't save much money, Uncle.'

'We'll start in a small way—there's a big demand for eggs, you know. Everyone's into eggs—scrambled, fried, poached or boiled. Egg curry for lunch.

Omelettes with dinner. Egg sandwiches for tea. How do you like your egg?'

'Fried,' I said. 'Sunny side up.'

The poultry farm never did happen, but it was good to be back in Dehra, with the prospect of limitless bicycle rides with Uncle Ken.